THE GREATEST TRIVIA QUIZ BOOK

The author would like to express thanks to Neal Townsend for moral support, Julia Ames and especially Tracy Craig for digital input, and a huge debt of gratitude to Doug Patmore for the loan of his brain in stickier moments.

This is a Parragon Book
First published in 2001

Parragon
Queen Street House
4 Queen Street
Bath BA1 1HE, UK

Photographs by kind permission of Ardea Ltd, Empics, Mirror Syndication, Pictorial Press. The author and publishers have made every reasonable effort to contact all copyright holders. Any errors that may have occurred are inadvertent and anyone who for any reason has not been contacted is invited to write to the publishers so that a full acknowledgement may be made in subsequent editions of this work.

Hardback ISBN: 0-75255-358-5
Paperback ISBN: 0-75256-814-0

Editorial, design and layout by Essential Books, 7 Stucley Place, London NW1 8NS

Printed and bound in China

THE GREATEST TRIVIA QUIZ BOOK

Compiled by Paul Rutterford

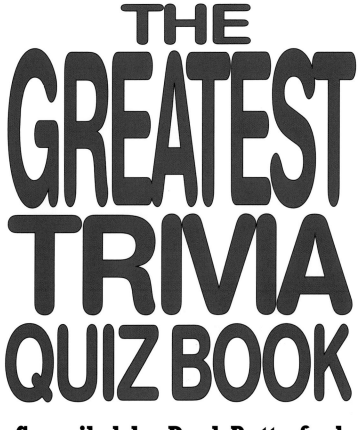

THE GREATEST TRIVIA QUIZ BOOK

QUIZ 1

13

1 Who was president at the time of the 1929 stock market crash?

2 Which future president drafted the Declaration of Independence?

3 By what name is president Lyndon B Johnson's wife Claudia better known?

4 Who was the first president to be born in the twentieth century?

5 How many presidents have been assassinated while in office?

6 Who, at 69, was the oldest president to take the oath of office?

7 Which president had the nickname 'Old Hickory'?

8 After being shot in 1912, which former president said of the assassination attempt, 'It takes more than that to kill a Bull Moose'?

9 Who is the only president buried in Washington, DC?

10 From whose inaugural speech do these words come: 'There is nothing wrong with America that cannot be cured by what is right with America'?

11 Who was the only president to serve in both World Wars?

12 Which president gave the first televised State of the Union address?

13 Which president was elected four consecutive times?

14 In 1858, three years before becoming president, Abraham Lincoln became senator of which state?

15 Which future president was the United States Representative to the United Nations under the Nixon administration?

16 Who was the first president to visit all fifty states?

17 Why was the 23rd president, Benjamin Harrison, called the 'Centennial President'?

18 Who was the first president to win the Nobel Peace Prize?

19 Which president said in a *Playboy* interview that he had 'committed adultery in my heart many times'?

20 How many states existed when George Washington took office?

21 What is the significance of the play *Our American Cousin*?

22 Who was the only president to serve two non-consecutive terms in office?

23 Whose presidential competency was questioned when he insisted during a debate that there was no Soviet domination in Poland?

24 Between the years 1857 and 1861, during James Buchanan's presidency, what role was performed by his niece, Harriet Lane, and why?

25 Which ex-president died in 1973, five days before an agreement was signed in Paris ending the fighting in Vietnam?

1 What was the name of Quint's boat in *Jaws*?

2 What is the name of the film company owned by Spielberg, Jeffrey Katzenberg and David Geffen?

3 What was the title of Spielberg's first feature film?

4 Which of Spielberg's films centres on a boy living in Shanghai at the outset of the Second World War?

5 What was the first Spielberg movie to be shot completely (exteriors as well as interiors) on soundstages?

6 Who came out of retirement to play the role of Richard Dreyfuss's spiritual guide in *Always*?

7 Who played the young Indy in *Indiana Jones and the Last Crusade*?

8 Which Spielberg movie featured the characters Sergeant Tree, Sitarski and 'Wild Bill' Kelso?

9 Which film director, much admired by Spielberg, played the role of a scientist in *Close Encounters of the Third Kind*?

10 Which of *The Color Purple*'s co-producers also wrote the music for the film?

11 Who played the part of Elliott's sister Gertie in *ET, The Extra-Terrestrial*?

12 During the shooting of *Schindler's List*, which other film was Spielberg editing from his hotel via satellite link?

13 Which film brought Spielberg his second Oscar for direction?

14 How was Spielberg 'credited' in the 1994 movie *The Flintstones*?

15 Which famous actress contributed some of the vocal effects to ET's voice?

16 Who played Dr Ellie Sattler in *Jurassic Park*?

17 In 1971, after two pilot episodes had been made, the then-23-year-old Spielberg directed the first regular installment of which TV detective show?

18 Who played Indy's love interest in *Indiana Jones and the Temple of Doom*, later to marry Spielberg himself?

19 Who has composed the music for the vast majority of Spielberg's films?

20 Of which book did Spielberg say, 'I read it and felt that I had been attacked. It terrified me, and I wanted to strike back'?

21 Who played the title role in the film *Hook*?

22 Which book did producer Kathleen Kennedy describe as 'one of those projects that was so obviously a Spielberg film'?

23 Which then-local talk show host played the role of Sofia in *The Color Purple*?

24 Although Spielberg directed *Raiders of the Lost Ark*, he did not have the final cut. Who did?

25 To what was Spielberg referring when he said, 'This is the best drink of water after the longest drought of my life'?

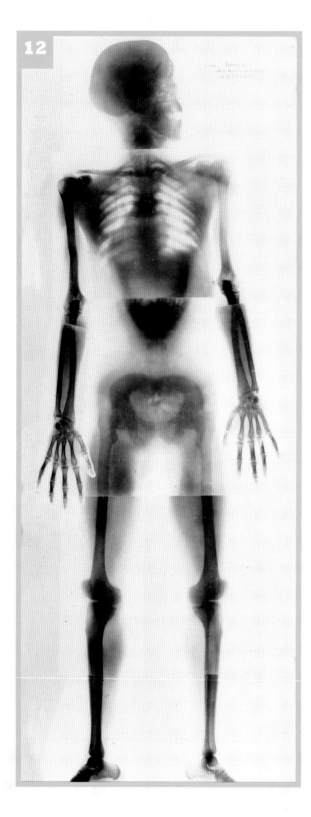

12

1 Which hormone regulates blood sugar level?

2 Where would you find carpal bones and tarsal bones respectively?

3 Caries is an extremely common disease. By what name is it better known?

4 In which organ are the hepatic arteries?

5 What is the condition called when an internal organ protrudes through the wall of the cavity in which it is normally contained?

6 Where in the body is the cochlea?

7 What is the essential difference between arteries and veins?

8 Where are the deltoid muscles?

9 What name is given to opacity in the lens of the eye?

10 Where is the pituitary gland?

11 What is the more common name for allergic rhinitis?

12 Of the two bones in the lower leg, the tibia and the fibula, which is the shinbone?

13 What are the pads of cartilage between spinal vertebrae commonly called?

14 Where are red blood cells formed?

15 Where is the temporal bone?

16 By what name is the tendon at the back of the ankle known?

17 Where is the coccyx?

20

18 Except for sex cells, all human cells contain twenty-three pairs of what?

19 What is the name given to an examination of a body by dissection to determine cause of death?

20 How many teeth should a person have?

21 Which sense is stimulated by the reaction of the olfactory cells?

22 What is the proper name for the kneecap?

23 Which gland produces hormones to control the body's metabolic rate?

24 Where is the carotid artery situated?

25 Which is the longest bone in the body?

1 What is the significance of the date 6 July 1957?

2 Which was the first single released by the Beatles on the Apple label?

3 On which Beatles song did George Harrison first play a sitar?

4 What is Paul McCartney's middle name?

5 Which was the first Beatles album to consist entirely of original material?

6 About whose sister is John Lennon's song 'Dear Prudence'?

7 Which sixties TV comedy show is mentioned on the *Sgt Pepper's Lonely Hearts Club Band* album?

8 From which band did the Beatles recruit Ringo Starr?

9 Who played lead guitar on George's 'While My Guitar Gently Weeps'?

10 Which single, when it peaked at number two in the UK charts in 1967, ended a run of eleven consecutive number ones?

11 In which American city did the Beatles play their last concert in 1966, vowing never to tour again?

12 Which album was at one time going to be called *Everest*?

13 What was the first Lennon–McCartney composition to feature Ringo on lead vocals?

14 Who were the Beatles accused of snubbing in Manila in 1966?

15 Which single was recorded at EMI's studios in Paris in 1964?

16 Who recorded a version of 'A Hard Day's Night' in the style of Laurence Olivier's *Richard III*?

17 Which song had the working title 'Scrambled Eggs'?

18 Which British prime ministers are mentioned in a Beatles song?

19 What was the title of John Lennon's second book?

20 Where did the Beatles appear on 30 January 1969?

21 Which one of the band's Hamburg friends designed the sleeve of the *Revolver* album?

22 Which Beatles song did Frank Sinatra describe as 'the greatest love song of the past fifty years'?

23 Who was the first Beatle to have a solo number one hit in the UK?

24 What contribution was made by Tony Gilbert, Sidney Sax, Kenneth Essex and Francisco Gabarro to the recording of the *Help!* album?

25 Which song from *The Beatles*, or 'The White Album' as it is commonly called, was originally titled 'Maharishi'?

25

1 Who was voted out of power in July 1943 after the invasion of Sicily?

2 In which year was the Women's Land Army formed?

3 In which country is El Alamein?

4 What was Operation Overlord?

5 Which country was invaded by the Japanese in 1937?

6 When General Douglas MacArthur told the Australian press 'I shall return', to where was he referring?

7 Who started arriving in Britain in January 1942?

8 Which two European countries fought each other between November 1939 and March 1940?

9 Which battle in the Pacific was fought between 4 and 5 June 1942?

10 Which German city was devastated by 2,600 tons of British bombs in February 1945?

11 Who was appointed to command the US Pacific fleet shortly after Pearl Harbor?

12 Who declared war on Japan the day before the bomb was dropped on Nagasaki?

13 What was Field Marshal Montgomery's first name?

14 Which Australian state capital was bombed by the Japanese in February 1942?

15 What happened aboard the USS *Missouri* on 2 September 1945?

16 What occurred between 26 May and 2 June 1940?

17 What was Operation Sealion?

18 Shostakovich's seventh symphony is named after which besieged Soviet city?

19 Who did Count Claus von Stauffenberg attempt to assassinate with a bomb on 20 July 1944?

20 Who replaced Winston Churchill at the Potsdam conference in July and August 1945?

21 Where did the British surrender to the Japanese in February 1942?

22 Which pilots were named after a typhoon which destroyed a Mongol invasion fleet bound for Japan in the Middle Ages?

23 Who succeeded Hitler as German leader?

24 What connected the countries of Eire, Portugal, Spain and Turkey during the war?

25 Which German word means 'lightning war'?

21

1 Which test batsman scored the most runs in the 1990s, with a total of 6,407?

2 Which wicket keeper has a record 389 dismissals in test cricket?

3 Which future West Indies captain made his debut against England in the 1953–54 series at the age of 17 years and 245 days?

4 With 131 test appearances, who is India's most capped player?

5 Which bowler has taken the most wickets in matches between England and Australia?

6 Who is the only bowler to take hat-tricks in successive tests?

7 In which season did Sri Lanka and Zimbabwe first meet in test cricket?

8 Who was the last England captain to regain the Ashes?

9 Who is the only batsman to score centuries in each of his first three tests?

10 On 15 March 1877, which ground was the venue for the first ever test match?

11 With an aggregate of 5,444 runs, who is New Zealand's highest scoring test batsman?

12 Which country did not play a test against England from 1965 to 1994?

13 Who is the only player to score a century and take five wickets in an innings on five separate occasions?

14 Of England's current test venues, which was the first to be used for test cricket?

15 Who scored a record 974 runs in a series against England in 1930?

16 In which season did India play their first series against Pakistan?

17 Who holds the record for the highest individual score in a test innings?

18 Which batsman has scored the most test centuries, with a total of 34?

19 Who scored a century off 56 deliveries for the West Indies against England in the 1985–86 series?

20 Which Indian bowler equalled Jim Laker's record of ten wickets in an innings when he dismissed Pakistan in the 1998–99 series?

21 Which currently available England player's father and grandfather both played for the West Indies?

22 Which country did Australia not play against between 1946 and 1973?

23 In the 1997–98 season, which country scored the highest ever innings total with 952 for 6 declared against India?

24 With 8,832 runs, who is Pakistan's leading test batsman?

25 Which two England players won their 100th caps in the same match against the West Indies in 2000?

1 What type of dead parrot did John Cleese take back to the pet shop?

2 Terry Jones played a man who claimed to have three what?

3 Which gang made Bolton 'a frightened city'?

4 On whose trail was Superintendent Harry 'Snapper' Organs?

5 What is it that 'nobody expects'?

6 In the Architects sketch, what did John Cleese's character propose instead of a block of flats?

7 What was the name of the cheese shop owner?

8 In the sketch involving Whistler, Wilde, Shaw and His Majesty, who played Oscar Wilde?

9 What does Michael Palin's lumberjack do on Wednesdays?

10 What did John Cleese try to sell from a tray in the cinema?

11 What did Graham Chapman complain about in the restaurant, provoking an over-the-top response from the entire staff?

12 What type of fish was John Cleese's character's pet, Eric?

13 Which pre-Python show was written by Eric Idle, Terry Jones and Michael Palin, in which they co-starred with Denise Coffey and David Jason?

14 Which member of the Python team was a doctor?

15 Which meat product was immortalised in song by the Pythons?

16 What did highwayman Dennis Moore demand from his victims?

17 What did the upper-class twits have to do to the dummies?

18 Who played the straight man to Eric Idle in the Nudge-Nudge sketch?

19 Which member of the Python team quit after the third series?

20 What is the significance of Bronzino's painting *Venus and Cupid*, which hangs in the National Gallery?

21 What character did Michael Palin change out of a superhero costume to become?

22 Which member of the team was responsible for Conrad Pooh's dancing teeth?

23 What is the title of the Monty Python theme tune?

24 In which town did Mr Hilter contest a local election?

25 What did Michael Palin's character want to be in the Vocational Guidance Counsellor sketch?

1 By what collective name were Moe Howard, Jerry 'Curly' Howard and Larry Fine better known?

2 Where were the three coins in Frank Sinatra's 1954 number one hit?

3 Who was the third man to set foot on the moon?

4 Who wrote *The Three Musketeers*?

5 Which chemical element has an atomic number of 3?

6 In the decathlon, which event comes third on the first day?

7 Where was the 1954 film *Three Coins in the Fountain* set?

8 Who directed the film *The Third Man*?

9 Which composer's third symphony is known as the *Eroica*?

10 Where does three appear between seventeen and nineteen?

11 Who had his only UK number one in 1960 with 'Three Steps to Heaven'?

12 Who was Henry VIII's third wife?

13 Who had a hit in 1977 with 'Three Times a Lady'?

14 What is the total of the three internal angles of a triangle?

15 Which disciple denied knowing Jesus Christ three times?

16 Which Philadelphia vocal group were favourites of Prince Charles?

17 Which cartoon character had three nephews called Huey, Dewey and Louie?

18 Where did Dawn singer Tony Orlando tell his loved one to 'knock three times' in the song of the same name?

19 Who was the third president of the United States of America?

20 Who wrote *Three Men in a Boat*?

21 Which rock music trio were filmed at their final concert at the Royal Albert Hall in 1968?

22 What is the world's third highest mountain?

23 In Shakespeare's play, who told Macbeth that he would eventually become king?

24 Who is third in line to the English throne?

25 Which three writers used the pseudonyms Currer, Ellis and Acton Bell?

11

ANSWERS TO QUIZ 1

US Presidents
1 Herbert Hoover
2 Thomas Jefferson
3 Lady Bird
4 John F Kennedy
5 Four: Lincoln, Garfield, McKinley and Kennedy
6 Ronald Reagan
7 Andrew Jackson
8 Theodore Roosevelt
9 Woodrow Wilson
10 Bill Clinton
11 Dwight D Eisenhower
12 Harry S Truman
13 Franklin D Roosevelt
14 Illinois
15 George Bush
16 Richard Nixon
17 He was inaugurated 100 years after George Washington
18 Theodore Roosevelt
19 Jimmy Carter
20 Thirteen
21 Abraham Lincoln was assassinated while watching the play
22 Grover Cleveland, 1885–89 and 1893–97
23 Gerald Ford
24 First Lady – Buchanan was a bachelor
25 Lyndon B Johnson

Steven Spielberg
1 The Orca
2 Dreamworks
3 *Duel*
4 *Empire of the Sun*
5 *Hook*
6 Audrey Hepburn
7 River Phoenix
8 *1941*
9 François Truffaut
10 Quincy Jones
11 Drew Barrymore
12 *Jurassic Park*
13 *Saving Private Ryan*
14 'Steven Spielrock presents'
15 Debra Winger
16 Laura Dern
17 *Columbo*
18 Kate Capshaw
19 John Williams
20 *Jaws*
21 Dustin Hoffman
22 *Jurassic Park*
23 Oprah Winfrey
24 Executive producer George Lucas
25 His Oscar for *Schindler's List*

The Human Body
1 Insulin
2 In the hands and feet
3 Tooth decay
4 The liver
5 A hernia
6 The inner ear
7 Arteries carry blood from the heart; veins return it
8 On the shoulder
9 A cataract
10 Under the brain
11 Hay fever
12 The tibia
13 Discs
14 In bone marrow
15 The side of the skull
16 The Achilles
17 At the base of the spine
18 Chromosomes
19 Autopsy
20 Thirty-two
21 Smell
22 The patella
23 The thyroid
24 In the neck
25 The femur

The Beatles
1 It was the day John Lennon first met Paul McCartney
2 'Hey Jude'
3 'Norwegian Wood (This Bird Has Flown)'
4 Paul – his first name is James
5 *A Hard Day's Night*
6 Mia Farrow's
7 *Meet the Wife* (on 'Good Morning, Good Morning')
8 Rory Storm and The Hurricanes
9 Eric Clapton
10 'Penny Lane/Strawberry Fields Forever'
11 San Francisco
12 *Abbey Road*
13 'I Wanna Be Your Man'
14 Imelda Marcos
15 'Can't Buy Me Love'
16 Peter Sellers
17 'Yesterday'
18 Mr Wilson and Mr Heath in 'Taxman'
19 *A Spaniard in the Works*
20 On the roof of the Apple offices in Savile Row, London
21 Klaus Voormann
22 'Something'
23 George Harrison with 'My Sweet Lord'
24 They were the string quartet on 'Yesterday'
25 'Sexy Sadie'

World War II
1 Mussolini
2 June 1939
3 Egypt
4 The 1944 Allied landings at Normandy
5 China
6 The Philippines
7 American GIs
8 The Soviet Union and Finland
9 The Battle of Midway
10 Dresden
11 Admiral Chester W Nimitz
12 The Soviet Union
13 Bernard
14 Darwin
15 Japan formally surrendered
16 The Dunkirk evacuation
17 Hitler's proposed invasion of Britain
18 Leningrad
19 Hitler
20 Clement Attlee
21 Singapore
22 The kamikaze
23 Admiral Donitz
24 They remained neutral along with Switzerland
25 Blitzkrieg

Test Cricket
1 Alec Stewart, England
2 Ian Healy, Australia
3 Garfield Sobers
4 Kapil Dev
5 Dennis Lillee
6 Wasim Akram, Pakistan v Sri Lanka, 1998–99
7 1994–95
8 David Gower, 1985
9 Mohammad Azharrudin, India v England, 1984–85
10 Melbourne Cricket Ground, Australia v England
11 Martin Crowe
12 South Africa
13 Ian Botham, England
14 The Oval, 1880
15 Donald Bradman, Australia
16 1952–53
17 Brian Lara, West Indies with 375
18 Sunil Gavaskar, India
19 Vivian Richards
20 Anil Kumble
21 Dean Headley
22 New Zealand
23 Sri Lanka
24 Javed Miandad
25 Michael Atherton and Alec Stewart

Monty Python
1 A Norwegian Blue
2 Buttocks
3 Hell's Grannies
4 Doug and Dinsdale Piranha
5 The Spanish Inquisition
6 A slaughterhouse
7 Mr Wensleydale
8 Graham Chapman
9 He goes shopping and has buttered scones for tea
10 An albatross
11 A dirty fork
12 An halibut
13 *Do Not Adjust Your Set*
14 Graham Chapman
15 Spam
16 Lupins
17 Remove their bras
18 Terry Jones
19 John Cleese
20 It contains the foot used in the title sequence
21 Bicycle Repair Man
22 Terry Gilliam
23 'The Liberty Bell'
24 Minehead, which he spells Meinhead
25 A lion tamer

The Number 3
1 The Three Stooges
2 In the fountain
3 Pete Conrad
4 Alexandre Dumas
5 Lithium
6 Shot put
7 Rome
8 Carol Reed
9 Beethoven
10 On a dartboard
11 Eddie Cochran
12 Jane Seymour
13 The Commodores
14 180 degrees
15 Peter
16 The Three Degrees
17 Donald Duck
18 On the ceiling
19 Thomas Jefferson
20 Jerome K Jerome
21 Cream
22 Kanchenjunga in the Himalayas
23 The three witches
24 Prince Henry
25 Charlotte, Emily and Anne Brontë

THE GREATEST TRIVIA QUIZ BOOK

QUIZ 2

17

1 Which Oscar-winning actress was born Susan Tomaling in 1946 and is known by her former married name?

2 By what name is the 16th-century painter Domenikos Theotokopoulos better known?

3 What is Alice Cooper's real name?

4 By what shorter name do we better know Czech-born actor Herbert Charles Angelo Kuchacevich de Schluderpacheru?

5 Which cigar-smoking, wisecracking comedian was born Nathan Birnbaum?

6 Under what name did Nigel John Davies shape the early career of Twiggy?

7 By what name do we better know Marion Michael Morrison?

8 Who has written books under the name Barbara Vine?

9 Which less-than-cuddly punk rock star was born John Richie?

10 Which British actor, of Dutch descent, was born Derek Van Den Bogaerd?

11 Which singer/actor was born Dino Crocetti in 1917?

12 Which American writer was born Samuel Langhorne Clemens?

13 Which novelist was born Mary Ann Evans?

14 What was the well-known pseudonym of Gertrud Margarete Zelle, who was executed as a German spy towards the end of World War I?

15 Which Hollywood actress, whose face was praised by Madonna in the song 'Vogue', was born Margarita Carmen Cansino in 1918?

16 The folk trio of Yarrow, Stookey and Travers became famous using just their first names. What are they?

17 Which movie star was born Lucille le Sueur?

18 By what name was American civil rights campaigner Malcolm Little better known?

19 By what name did bodybuilder Angelo Siciliano become famous?

20 Actor Stewart Granger had to change his name because his real name was the same as which leading Hollywood star?

21 By what name was the British broadcaster William Joyce, a Nazi propagandist during World War II, known?

22 Remembered chiefly for his tough-guy roles, what was the screen name of Emanuel Goldenberg?

23 Which American actor was born Ramón Estevez in 1940?

24 Which Jamaican singer, who has had two UK number one hit singles, was born Orville Richard Burrell?

25 Which famous 19th-century author wrote under the name Ellis Bell?

3

1 In which two films did Emma Thompson win Oscars as leading actress and for adapted screenplay in 1992 and 1995 respectively?

2 In which year was an award for best sound first given?

3 Which Oscar winner lends his voice to the animated series *South Park*?

4 Which actor won two consecutive leading actor Oscars in the 1990s?

5 For which film did David Lean receive his first Oscar as director?

6 In which 1942 film did Irving Berlin's 'White Christmas' win the award for best song?

7 Which Alfred Hitchcock film won the best picture Oscar in 1940?

8 Which actress, mother of a British rock star, won a special Oscar in 1960 for outstanding juvenile performance in the movie *Pollyanna*?

9 For his performance in which film did Kevin Kline win the best supporting actor Oscar in 1988?

10 In 1948, which father and son won Academy Awards for the same movie, as supporting actor and director respectively?

11 Which two leading ladies tied for the best actress Oscar in 1968?

12 Which film, a mixture of live action and animation, won four Oscars in 1988?

13 Which British actress won two Oscars for leading roles in the 1970s?

14 What is the connection between 1981's best director and 1983's best leading actress?

15 For which animated short film did Nick Park win his first Oscar in 1990?

16 Gene Hackman won his second Oscar in 1996 as supporting actor in *Unforgiven*. For which 1971 movie did he win the best actor award?

17 Who famously broke down in tears during her acceptance speech at the 1998 awards ceremony?

18 For his role in which film did Michael Douglas receive the best actor award in 1987?

19 Which multi-Oscar-winning movie of the 1970s did Michael Douglas co-produce?

20 Jason Robards won his second consecutive Oscar as supporting actor in 1977 for *Julia*. For his role in which tense political thriller did he win in 1976?

21 For which 1970s movie did Francis Ford Coppola win the best director Oscar?

22 In which year were the supporting actor and actress categories introduced?

23 Which actor, born with the surname Coppola, won the best actor Oscar in 1995?

24 Which great singer won the best supporting actor award in 1953?

25 Which director won an Oscar for his first film in 2000?

1 Through which European capital city does the River Tagus flow?

2 In which city does the Blue Nile meet the White Nile?

3 Which river forms the border between Mexico and Texas?

4 On which river does Belfast stand?

5 The Orange river flows into the Atlantic Ocean between which two southern African countries?

6 Into which body of water does the River Volga flow?

7 On which river would you find the Victoria Falls and the Kariba dam?

8 The Putumayo, the Purus and the Madeira are three of the many tributaries of which great South American river?

9 Which Australian river forms most of the border between New South Wales and Victoria?

10 On which river do the cities of Florence and Pisa stand?

11 Which river featured in the musical *Showboat*?

12 At nearly 4,000 miles, Asia's longest river is the Chang Jiang. By what name is it better known in the West?

13 Into which body of water do the Tigris and the Euphrates flow?

14 Which rivers flow on either side of Manhattan Island?

15 Which river rises in Tibet and flows through China, Burma, Laos, Thailand, Cambodia and Vietnam before reaching the South China Sea?

16 From which South American country does the Orinoco flow into the Atlantic?

17 Which Asian city's international airport is built at the mouth of the Tama-gawa?

18 Which two capital cities stand on the mouth of the Rio de la Plata, or River Plate?

19 On which river does Inverness stand?

20 Which river flows through the Grand Canyon?

21 The Mackenzie river in Canada's North West Territories flows north into the Beaufort Sea. What does it cross along the way?

22 In which country does the Rhine reach the sea?

23 Through which country does the River Dnieper flow before it reaches the Black Sea?

24 Which river is spanned by Britain's longest suspension bridge?

25 Which river flows between Lake Ontario and Lake Erie and forms part of the border between Canada and the United States?

20

1 With which particular instrument would you associate Gerry Mulligan?

2 In which city would you find jazz clubs called Birdland, the Blue Note, and the Village Vanguard?

3 Who is generally credited with freeing the role of the jazz guitar to that of a solo instrument?

4 Whose trumpet was recognisable by the way it was bent out of shape?

5 Which band was formed in the 1970s by former Miles Davis band members Joe Zawinul and Wayne Shorter?

6 Written by Billy Strayhorn, what was the signature tune of the Duke Ellington band?

7 Which band featured among its members Joe Sample, Wayne Henderson and Wilton Felder?

8 With whom did Louis Armstrong sing about the virtues of jazz in the musical *High Society*?

9 With which instrument would you associate Lionel Hampton, Red Norvo and Gary Burton?

10 What was the name given to duels between soloists, where they would improvise head to head until one took a clear advantage?

11 Whose albums include *Kind of Blue*, *In a Silent Way*, *Bitches Brew* and *Tutu*?

12 Which saxophonist was known as 'Bird'?

13 What name is given to the type of singing that mimics an instrumental solo?

14 Over four decades, which drummer led a band called the Jazz Messengers?

8

15 With which instrument would you associate Tommy Dorsey, Glenn Miller and Trummy Young?

16 Which British guitarist fronted the Mahavishnu Orchestra?

17 Which trumpeter, born in 1961, enjoys equally successful jazz and classical careers?

18 Which singer was discovered in the 1930s after winning a singing contest at Harlem's Apollo Theatre?

19 Which keyboard player had an 'Arkestra' and claimed to have come from another planet?

20 James P Johnson wrote the signature to which 1920s dance craze?

21 Which band leader/composer/producer wrote the score for the 1967 movie *In the Heat of the Night*, featuring Ray Charles on the title song?

22 Who was the first black singer to host his own TV programme?

23 Which British sax player fronts the band Paraphernalia?

24 By what name is pianist Ferdinand Joseph Lemott remembered?

25 Which style of jazz was pioneered by Charlie Parker and Dizzy Gillespie?

14

18

1 By how many days did Roald Amundsen's team beat that of Captain Scott to the South Pole in 1911?

2 What was Italian mountaineer Reinhold Messner the first man to achieve in 1980?

3 Which entertainer has won two Oscars, five Emmys, seven Grammys, seven Golden Globes and a Special Tony?

4 Which event in 1985 raised around $80 million for Ethiopian famine relief?

5 What was achieved by Briton Brian Jones and Swiss Bertrand Piccard in March 1999?

6 Discovered in a German disco at seventeen, who has appeared on more magazine covers than any other model?

7 What was the name of the driver of Thrust SSC which broke the land speed record in Nevada in 1997?

8 Which British sportsman won his fifth consecutive Olympic gold medal at the Sydney games?

9 Which country has the world's largest volunteer ambulance organisation?

10 Which violinist played with the San Francisco symphony orchestra in 1926 at the age of nine?

11 Which landmark was first reached by a team led by American Robert Edwin Peary in 1909?

12 What was the name of the raft on which Norwegian Thor Heyerdahl crossed the Pacific from Peru to Polynesia in 1947?

13 What body-monitoring device won inventor Godfrey Hounsfield the 1979 Nobel Prize for medicine?

14 Who retired undefeated as heavyweight champion of the world in 1956 after forty-nine professional fights?

15 Which land speed barrier was broken by Major Henry Seagrave in 1927?

16 What did Ulster women Betty Williams and Mairead Corrigan win in 1977?

17 In 1998 a team of doctors at the University of Pittsburgh Medical Center carried out the first transplant operation of its kind. What was it?

18 What was the name of Neil Armstrong and Buzz Aldrin's colleague aboard the orbiting command module?

19 Which actor won a posthumous Oscar in 1977?

20 Who held all four tennis Grand Slam titles plus the Olympic title in 1988?

21 Who, in 1922, became the first man to swim the 100 metres freestyle in less than 60 seconds?

18

22 Who, in May 1967, completed a solo round-the-world trip in a yacht called *Gypsy Moth IV*?

23 Which cyclist came back from cancer treatment to win the Tour de France?

24 What was special about the drive taken by Americans David Scott and James Irwin on 31 July 1971?

25 Which athlete set world records for the 800 metres, the mile and the 1500 metres within a six-week period in 1979?

11

1 For which team was Jean Alesi driving when he won the 1995 Canadian Grand Prix?

2 What connects the Spanish Grand Prix of 1981 with that of 1997?

3 Who won the first Malaysian Grand Prix?

4 Which Austrian driver made his debut in his home Grand Prix in 1971, driving for March?

5 Which female driver made twelve Grand Prix starts between 1974 and 1976?

6 Who retired from Formula One after winning his third Formula One title in 1973?

7 At which circuits would you find: a) Abbey Curve b) Adelaide and c) Clark Kurve?

8 Who is the only driver to win the Formula One title posthumously?

9 Who drove in 256 Grands Prix between 1977 and 1993, winning six races?

10 Which current TV presenter drove in the 1980 Belgian Grand Prix?

11 How many times did Graham Hill win at Monaco?

12 For whom did Italian-American Mario Andretti drive when he won the 1978 title?

13 Where did Juan Manuel Fangio win his first and his last Grand Prix?

14 How many Grand Prix wins did Damon Hill achieve?

15 Which Formula One driver, whose own team began racing in 1966 and is one of the major teams of today, was killed at Goodwood in 1970?

16 Who won all six races in the 1952 season?

17 In what way was Ireland successful in the 1961 United States Grand Prix?

18 Which German driver made his Formula One debut in Brazil in 1994, and won his first race at San Marino in 1997?

19 In which year was the Australian Grand Prix last staged at Adelaide, before being switched to Melbourne?

20 For which team did Michael Schumacher drive in his first Grand Prix in Belgium in 1991?

21 Between 1981 and 1991, which two Brazilian drivers won the Formula One title six times between them?

22 How many races did Nigel Mansell win in his championship-winning year of 1992?

23 Which driver drove a Lotus in all twenty-five of his Grand Prix victories in the 1960s?

24 Who was the only Formula One champion to have also been world motorcycling champion?

25 Who retired at the end of the 1993 season, having taken his fourth Formula One title?

1 What is the name of Phoebe's identical twin sister?

2 Which of the characters had a relationship with Dr Richard Burke, as played by Tom Selleck?

3 What particular contribution is made to the show by Michael Skloff and Allee Willis?

4 What is the name of Chandler's ex-girlfriend with the irritating laugh?

5 What is Ross's profession?

6 When Joey moved to his own apartment, what was the name of Chandler's new room-mate?

7 At which famous department store did Rachel get a job?

8 Who did the cast prod with their giant poking device made from old chopsticks?

9 Whose parents are played by Christina Pickles and Elliott Gould?

10 What is the name of the coffee shop?

11 What is the title of Phoebe's best-known song?

12 What were Joey and Chandler's two unusual pets?

13 What are the names of Ross's first wife and her partner?

14 Which regular supporting character is played by James Michael Tyler?

15 What was the name of the soap opera in which Joey played the part of neurosurgeon Dr Drake Ramoray?

16 What type of animal was Marcel?

17 In the London episodes, who played the part of a souvenir vendor?

18 With which cast member was actor Tate Donovan romantically linked after appearing on the show?

19 Who were the two team captains for the Thanksgiving football match?

20 Who played the part of Emily's mother?

21 Where did Ross and Rachel finally consummate their relationship?

22 How did Chandler refer to his 'third nipple'?

23 Which one of the characters dated multi-millionaire Pete Becker?

24 What was the name of Ross's girlfriend who he met on his trip to China?

25 After Chandler moved in with Monica, who guested as Joey's new room-mate, Janine?

1 What name is given to a person who shoes horses, and which can also be another name for veterinary surgeon, or a non-commissioned officer who looks after horses in a cavalry regiment?

2 What is a lepidopterist?

3 What was the name given to a boy who carried a torch for pedestrians in dark streets?

4 In which branch of medicine does an oncologist work?

5 What does a lapidary do?

6 What is the colloquial term for a travelling salesman for a firm specialising in hire purchase?

7 A person employed to do all sorts of work is given what Latin-based name?

8 A medical practitioner specialising in the diagnosis and treatment of eye diseases used to be called an oculist. What is the name used now?

9 What is a bonze?

10 In which occupation might you be called a bluejacket?

11 What would a lithologist study?

12 What does a funambulist walk on?

13 What would a hagiologist write about?

14 What slang term is used for a criminal who specialises in safecracking?

15 In America he is called a longshoreman. What is the UK equivalent?

16 What occupation was used by Lennon and McCartney for the name of one of their early bands?

17 What was sold once by a colporteur?

18 What does a dendrologist study?

19 Why is a colour-sergeant so called?

20 What term is used for a person who illegally makes and/or smuggles distilled liquor?

21 What familiar word, sometimes humorously associated with lightning, describes a person who rides the near horse of a team of horses drawing a coach?

22 What does a milliner make?

23 Who would be involved in the scientific study of the origin, history, structure, and composition of the earth?

24 What word for a labourer originates from the days of canal building when it was important that the labourers knew where they were going?

25 In which country does a gaucho herd cattle?

ANSWERS TO QUIZ 2

Real Names
1 Susan Sarandon
2 El Greco
3 Vincent Furnier
4 Herbert Lom
5 George Burns
6 Justin de Villeneuve
7 John Wayne
8 P D James
9 Sid Vicious
10 Dirk Bogarde
11 Dean Martin
12 Mark Twain
13 George Eliot
14 Mata Hari
15 Rita Hayworth
16 Peter, Paul and Mary
17 Joan Crawford
18 Malcolm X
19 Charles Atlas
20 James Stewart
21 Lord Haw-Haw
22 Edward G Robinson
23 Martin Sheen
24 Shaggy
25 Emily Brontë

The Oscars
1 *Howards End* and *Sense and Sensibility*
2 1930
3 Isaac Hayes ('Theme from *Shaft*', 1971)
4 Tom Hanks (*Philadelphia* in 1993 and *Forrest Gump* in 1994)
5 *The Bridge on the River Kwai*
6 *Holiday Inn*
7 *Rebecca*
8 Hayley Mills
9 *A Fish Called Wanda*
10 Walter and John Huston (*The Treasure of the Sierra Madre*)
11 Katharine Hepburn (*The Lion in Winter*) and Barbra Streisand (*Funny Girl*)
12 *Who Framed Roger Rabbit?*
13 Glenda Jackson (*Women in Love* in 1970 and *A Touch of Class* in 1973)
14 They are brother and sister; Warren Beatty and Shirley MacLaine
15 *Creature Comforts*
16 *The French Connection*
17 Gwyneth Paltrow
18 *Wall Street*
19 *One Flew over the Cuckoo's Nest*
20 *All the President's Men*
21 *The Godfather, Part II*
22 1936

23 Nicolas Cage (*Leaving Las Vegas*)
24 Frank Sinatra (*From Here to Eternity*)
25 Sam Mendes (*American Beauty*)

Rivers
1 Lisbon
2 Khartoum
3 The Rio Grande
4 The Lagan
5 Namibia and South Africa
6 The Caspian Sea
7 The Zambesi
8 The Amazon
9 The Murray
10 The Arno
11 The Mississippi
12 The Yangtze
13 The Gulf
14 The Hudson and the East River
15 The Mekong
16 Venezuela
17 Tokyo
18 Buenos Aires and Montevideo
19 The Ness
20 The Colorado
21 The Arctic Circle
22 The Netherlands
23 Ukraine
24 The Humber
25 The Niagara

Jazz
1 Baritone sax
2 New York
3 Charlie Christian
4 Dizzy Gillespie
5 Weather Report
6 'Take the "A" Train'
7 The Crusaders
8 Bing Crosby
9 Vibraphone
10 Cutting contests
11 Miles Davis
12 Charlie Parker
13 Scat singing
14 Art Blakey
15 Trombone
16 John McLaughlin
17 Wynton Marsalis
18 Ella Fitzgerald
19 Sun Ra
20 The Charleston
21 Quincy Jones
22 Nat 'King' Cole
23 Barbara Thompson
24 Jelly Roll Morton
25 Bebop

Human Achievement
1 33 days
2 He climbed Everest solo
3 Barbra Streisand
4 Live Aid
5 First non-stop round-the-world trip in a hot air balloon
6 Claudia Schiffer
7 Andy Green
8 Steve Redgrave
9 Pakistan
10 Yehudi Menuhin
11 The North Pole
12 Kon-Tiki
13 The CAT scanner
14 Rocky Marciano
15 200 mph
16 The Nobel Peace Prize
17 They transplanted brain cells
18 Michael Collins
19 Peter Finch
20 Steffi Graf
21 Johnny Weissmuller
22 Francis Chichester
23 Lance Armstrong
24 They were the first men to drive on the moon
25 Sebastian Coe

Formula One
1 Ferrari
2 They were won by father and son, Gilles and Jacques Villeneuve
3 Eddie Irvine
4 Nikki Lauda
5 Lella Lombardi
6 Jackie Stewart
7 a) Silverstone b) Magny-Cours c) Hockenheim
8 Jochen Rindt, 1970
9 Riccardo Patrese
10 Tiff Needell
11 Five: 1963, 1964, 1965, 1968 and 1969
12 John Player Lotus
13 Monaco 1950 and Germany 1957
14 Twenty-two
15 Bruce McLaren
16 Alberto Ascari
17 The winning driver was Innes Ireland
18 Heinz-Harald Frentzen
19 1995
20 Jordan
21 Nelson Piquet 1981, 1983, and 1987; and Ayrton Senna 1988, 1990, and 1991
22 Nine
23 Jim Clark
24 John Surtees
25 Alain Prost

Friends
1 Ursula
2 Monica
3 Together they wrote the show's theme song
4 Janice
5 Palaeontologist
6 Eddie
7 Bloomingdales
8 Ugly naked guy
9 Ross and Monica
10 Central Perk
11 'Smelly Cat'
12 A chick and a duck
13 Carol and Susan
14 Gunther at Central Perk
15 *Days of Our Lives*
16 A monkey
17 Richard Branson
18 Jennifer Aniston
19 Ross and Monica
20 Jennifer Saunders
21 Under a rug at the museum
22 A nubbin
23 Monica
24 Julie
25 Elle Macpherson

Occupations
1 Farrier
2 One who studies butterflies or moths
3 A linkboy
4 Cancer/tumour treatment
5 Works or deals in precious stones
6 A tallyman
7 A factotum
8 Ophthalmologist
9 A (Japanese or Chinese) Buddhist priest
10 A sailor
11 Rocks/stones
12 A tightrope
13 Saints
14 Peterman
15 A stevedore
16 Quarrymen
17 Books, especially Bibles
18 Trees and shrubs
19 He has responsibility for carrying a regimental or national flag
20 Moonshiner
21 Postillion
22 Hats
23 A geologist
24 Navvy (from navigator)
25 Argentina

THE GREATEST TRIVIA QUIZ BOOK

QUIZ 3

1 The novel *Children of the New Forest* by Captain Marryat was set during which conflict?

2 Who is the eldest of actor John Mills's three children?

3 What relation is Princess Beatrice to Peter Philips?

4 How old was Shirley Temple when she appeared in her first short film?

5 What was the brand name of the unsuccessful Ford car that was named after Henry Ford's son?

6 Caesarion was the child of Julius Caesar and which famous woman?

7 Peter, Phyllis and Roberta were collectively known as what in the title of a book by E Nesbit?

8 What was the real name of the man whose son was known as Baby Doc?

9 What was the forename of William Shakespeare's son?

10 Which rock star named his daughter Moon Unit?

11 In Dickens's *A Christmas Carol*, who was Tiny Tim's father?

12 Actor Martin Sheen has two sons. What are their names?

13 Christabel was one of suffragette leader Emmeline Pankhurst's two daughters. What was the name of the other?

14 What was the name of Pinocchio's creator-cum-father?

15 Which musical gangster movie had a cast made up entirely of children?

16 In which children's book will you meet Charlie Bucket?

17 What was the name of the ill-fated Czar Nicholas II's youngest daughter?

18 Which British actor is the son of a former Attorney General?

19 Cedric Errol was the given name of which eponymous child hero of a 19th-century novel?

20 Which film star thoughtfully named his daughter Sage Moonblood?

21 Whose daughter was nicknamed 'Thunderthighs'?

22 Which band had a hit with 'Little Children' in the 1960s?

23 Which daughter of James V of Scotland met an untimely death?

24 Who was the famous son of Jennie Jerome?

25 His hair is on the long side but he certainly doesn't come from Liverpool. Who is he?

25

1 Which Edith Wharton novel has been filmed three times, most recently by Martin Scorsese in 1993?

2 What was the title of Milos Forman's 1989 film based on the novel *Les Liaisons Dangereuses*?

3 Which writer/director adapted *The Great Gatsby* for the 1974 film version?

4 What was the title of the Stanley Kubrick film based on the novel *Red Alert*?

5 The movie *One Flew Over the Cuckoo's Nest* was made in 1975. In which year was Ken Kesey's novel published?

6 In 1971 Doubleday publishers received an outline of a novel called *A Stillness in the Water*. What was the book, and film, eventually called?

7 By what title do we know the 1979 film based on Joseph Conrad's novel *Heart of Darkness*?

8 In 1939 *Heart of Darkness* was supposed to have been the directorial debut of which actor/writer/director?

9 On which Jane Austen novel was the 1996 comedy *Clueless* based?

10 Who played author Paul Sheldon in the film of Stephen King's *Misery*?

11 The title role in which controversial story was played by Sue Lyon in 1962 and by Dominique Swain in 1997?

12 Which James M Cain novel was turned into a film in 1944 by director Billy Wilder and starred Fred MacMurray, Barbara Stanwyck and Edward G Robinson?

13 Which Alfred Hitchcock film, from a Robert Bloch book, did director Gus Van Sant remake virtually shot-for-shot in 1998?

14 Which actor made his final screen appearance in 1984 in the film *1984*?

15 What was the full title of the H G Wells story that formed the basis of the film *Things to Come*?

16 What was Stephen King's first novel, published in 1974 and made into a film by Brian de Palma two years later?

17 Which film did Ridley Scott make from Philip K Dick's novel *Do Androids Dream of Electric Sheep?*?

18 In the context of this section, what connects directors George Cukor, David Lean, Ronald Neame and Carol Reed?

19 What connects the films *The Bridge on the River Kwai* and *Planet of the Apes*?

20 What was the title of Quentin Tarantino's film based on Elmore Leonard's book *Rum Punch*?

21 Which Herman Melville novel was first filmed in 1926 as *The Sea Beast*?

22 Which Alexandre Dumas novel has featured, in three of its filmed versions, Douglas Fairbanks, Louis Jourdan and Gabriel Byrne as d'Artagnan?

23 Which 1960 Pulitzer Prize-winning novel spawned a 1962 movie in which Gregory Peck gave an Oscar-winning performance?

24 Which science fiction movie was based on an Arthur C Clarke short story called 'The Sentinel'?

25 Which film is based on a James Jones novel set in Honolulu prior to the attack on Pearl Harbor?

23

1 What is the name for a line on a weather map which connects points of equal temperature?

2 What is the central area of a hurricane called?

3 What is an anemometer?

4 Which warm, dry wind is prevalent along the eastern edge of the Rocky Mountains, whose name means 'snow eater'?

5 What does the abbreviation CFC stand for?

6 Which gas is most prevalent in the earth's atmosphere?

7 In which desert does the wind known as the Sirocco originate?

8 What occurs between a negatively charged cloud base and positively charged earth below?

9 What is the common name for wispy cirrus clouds?

10 What name is given to the dividing line between advancing cold air and a mass of warmer air?

11 Which layer of the atmosphere lies between heights of approximately six-and-a-half miles and thirty miles above the earth's surface?

12 Occurring twice yearly, what name is given to a day that consists of twelve hours of daylight and twelve hours of darkness?

13 What name is given to westerly winds found in the southern hemisphere between forty and fifty degrees latitude?

14 Usually occurring in summer, what name is given to a mass of cloud that is fractured into a pattern of ripples?

15 Which Pacific Ocean weather condition brings unusually high water temperature and was given its name by Peruvian fishermen?

16 What nationality was Anders Celsius, who devised the Centigrade scale of temperature measurement?

17 What is the name given to the weather feature in which the atmospheric pressure is lower than that of the surrounding air?

18 In India, what name is given to the period between June and September when about seventy-five percent of the region's annual rainfall arrives?

19 Which vital part of the atmosphere makes up about seven millionths of its volume?

20 According to the Beaufort Scale, how many miles per hour must a wind reach to be classified as a hurricane?

21 When lightning strikes, the air along its path heats up very quickly and very intensely. What is produced by this sudden expansion of air?

22 What name is given to a prolonged period of unusually hot weather well above the average for a particular region?

23 How far above the earth's surface do cirrus clouds form?

24 What name is given to the layer of ground that remains permanently frozen despite seasonal changes in temperature?

25 At what temperature does the Fahrenheit scale give the same reading as the Celsius, or Centigrade scale?

21

1 Which singing cowboy was born Leonard Slye, and whose early career was as part of the Sons of the Pioneers group?

2 Who wrote the song 'Coat of Many Colours', about a girl ridiculed for the coat her mother made for her from fabric scraps?

3 How old was LeAnn Rimes when she had her first number one country album?

4 With which band is Raul Malo the lead singer?

5 Which successful solo artist is the regular host of the Country Music Awards?

6 Which guitarist replaced Bernie Leadon in the Eagles in 1975?

7 Who was the first woman to be inducted into the Country Music Hall of Fame in 1973, ten years after her death?

8 Which singer is known as 'The Man in Black'?

9 Which fiddle-playing singer is backed by the band Union Station?

10 Which singer started as a session guitarist, working with the likes of Bobby Darin, Frank Sinatra, Dean Martin and the Beach Boys?

11 Who was declared dead on New Year's Day 1953, at the age of twenty-nine?

12 Who wrote the songs 'Oh, Lonesome Me', 'Sweet Dreams' and 'I Can't Stop Loving You'?

13 Which female trio released the multi-platinum album *Wide Open Spaces* in 1998?

14 Who released an album in the guise of a fictitious singer entitled *In the Life of Chris Gaines* in 1999?

15 Which singer/songwriter appeared in the movie *The Player*, where he met his wife-to-be Julia Roberts?

16 Which guitarist joined RCA in 1947 and was put in charge of the label's Nashville studio in 1955, where he helped further the careers of, among others, Jim Reeves, Don Gibson and Elvis Presley?

17 Which singer is the younger sister of Loretta Lynn?

16

18 With which instrument is Earl Scruggs associated?

19 Which country singer had a song named after him on Prefab Sprout's 1985 album *Steve McQueen*?

20 Which member of the Monkees went on to front the First National Band?

21 Which two singers married in 1969, divorced in 1975, and recorded one last album together in 1995?

22 Whose albums include *Copperhead Road*, *Guitar Town* and *Train A Comin'*?

23 Born Roberta Streeter, whose first single was the strange 'Ode to Billy Joe', about a young man's suicide?

24 The song 'Crazy' is synonymous with Patsy Cline, but who wrote it?

25 Who was a member of the Byrds and the Flying Burrito Brothers, and recorded the solo albums *GP* and *Grievous Angel*?

1 What is the name given to a simulated three-dimensional environment using computer graphics?

2 Which stock control system was introduced in American supermarkets in 1974?

3 Which German company introduced the interrupter gear, enabling a machine gun to fire through an aeroplane's propeller?

4 What fundamental part of computer technology was patented in the US in 1961?

5 In which country was the portable domestic electric room heater first marketed in 1912?

6 In 1937 American engineer Chester Carlson invented a process called xerography. What is its more common name?

7 In which country did polyethylene plastic go into commercial production in 1939?

8 In which decade did the British Post Office introduce a telex service?

9 Which Dutch company began marketing compact disc players in 1982?

10 Developed in the United States in 1930, by what name is polyvinyl chloride plastic better known?

11 What diameter floppy disks were introduced by IBM in 1970?

12 In which country was fuel injection for cars introduced in 1954?

13 In 1976 JVC introduced the VHS video format. What do the initials stand for?

14 What widely used kitchen item was first marketed by the General Electric Company in 1909?

15 What advance in sound recording was made by British engineer Alan Blumlein in 1933?

16 Which American architect/engineer invented geodesic dome construction?

17 What type of hook and eye fastening was invented by Swiss engineer Georges de Mestral in 1948, and introduced commercially in 1956?

18 In which year were tissue cells first grown outside the body by US biologist Ross Harrison?

19 In which year was the car seat belt patented?

20 In which year did the worldwide computer network begin operation?

21 Scotch tape was invented in 1930 by American Richard Drew. For which company did he work?

22 Name the kitchen development patented by American radar engineer Percy Spencer in 1945.

23 The lightweight portable electric drill was first marketed in 1917 by two American inventors with the first names Duncan and Alonso. What were their surnames?

24 What type of engine was invented by German Felix Wankel in 1929?

25 What communication aid was invented in 1905 by American undertaker Almon Strowger?

12

1 Which Spanish team plays at the Vicente Calderón stadium?

2 Who is the older, by about fifteen minutes, of the Dutch twins Ronald and Frank De Boer?

3 Which German team won the European Cup three years in succession from 1974?

4 From which Italian team did Tottenham Hotspur sign Jimmy Greaves in 1961?

5 Which English manager once played his home games at the Volksparkstadion on the outskirts of Hamburg?

6 Who did eventual winners Denmark replace just before the start of the 1992 European Championships?

7 Which Scotsman managed Turkish club Galatasaray in the mid-1990s?

8 Which club's stadium has the largest capacity in Europe?

9 Who did France beat in the semifinal of Euro 2000?

10 What is meant by the name Steaua, as in Steaua Bucharest?

11 Which Norwegian club plays in the city of Trondheim?

12 By what score did Hungary, featuring Ferenc Puskas, beat England in their first ever Wembley defeat in 1953?

13 Which company is the sponsor of Dutch club PSV Eindhoven?

14 To what did Dinamo Zagreb change their name after independence in 1992?

15 Who did Borussia Dortmund beat in the final to lift the European Cup for the first time in 1997?

16 Sunderland's Stadium of Light takes its name from that of which other European team?

17 Whose arrival at Napoli spurred the team on to its first Italian league title in 1987?

18 Slovan Bratislava last won the Czechoslovakian league title in 1992. Which league title did they win in 1994?

19 Which two Englishmen have scored in the last two (1999 and 2000) European Cup finals?

20 Which European city has teams with the names CSKA, Dynamo, Spartak and Torpedo?

21 Which player moved from Barcelona to Real Madrid for a record transfer fee in the summer of 2000?

22 Which French side has its home at the Parc des Princes?

23 Who had Manchester United been playing prior to the Munich air disaster in 1958?

24 What nationality is Jean-Marc Bosman, after whom the transfer ruling is named?

25 With which Italian club do you associate Welshman Ian Rush, Irishman Liam Brady, and Frenchman Michel Platini?

1 Who originally starred alongside Dennis Franz in *NYPD Blue*?

2 In the British-made *Sherlock Holmes* series shown in the eighties and nineties, who played the title role?

3 Which programme's lead character was detective Steve McGarrett?

4 What is Chief Inspector Morse's Christian name?

5 Who had a 1981 hit with the theme tune from *Hill Street Blues*?

6 Name one of the two future Munsters who starred in the 1960s cop comedy *Car 54, Where Are You?*

7 In which show were the assembled officers advised by Sergeant Esterhaus to 'be careful out there'?

8 Who played the part of Stavros in *Kojak*?

9 Which TV cop had a US and UK number 1 with 'Don't Give Up On Us'?

10 Who played the lead role in the early 1970s American show *Dan August*?

11 Which 1987 film saw Columbo's Peter Falk narrating an unconventional fairy tale to a bed-ridden boy?

12 Which 1970s TV cop show made a star of Michael Douglas?

13 Which musical police show was the brainchild of writer/producer Steven Bochco?

14 Which series starred Larry Wilcox and Erik Estrada as officers Jon Baker and Frank 'Ponch' Poncherello?

15 Which well-known TV series about crime-fighters was brought to the big screen in 1987, starring Kevin Costner?

16 From which 1970s cop show does the catchphrase 'Book 'em, Dan-O' hail?

17 What was the setting for the series *Magnum, PI*?

18 Who were the best known subordinates of Chief Inspector Frank Haskins in a British series of the 1970s?

19 What 1971 film saw Paul Michael Glaser as suitor to one of Topol's daughters?

20 Which of *Columbo* star Peter Falk's eyes is the false one?

21 Who played opposite Tyne Daly in the pilot episode of 1980s series *Cagney and Lacey*?

22 Which wheelchair-bound policeman was played by Raymond Burr from 1967 to 1975 in the USA?

23 Which show had central characters called Maddie Hayes and David Addison?

24 In the TV version of *In the Heat of the Night*, who played the role of Police Chief Bill Gillespie, made famous by Rod Steiger in the original film?

25 Which police comedy series spawned the *Naked Gun* movies?

1 Which member of the British royal family helped popularise items such as Fair Isle sweaters, suede shoes and dinner jackets?

2 Which British designer popularised the minidress in the 1960s?

3 Born in Saumur, France in 1883, by what name is Gabrielle Bonheur better known?

4 In which year did Giorgio Armani establish his own company?

5 Who was appointed dressmaker to the Queen in 1955?

6 In 1947 whose first collection under his own name was dubbed the New Look?

7 Who presented a collection called Pirate in 1981, with her then partner Malcolm McLaren?

8 Which designer was responsible for the trend of slogan-bearing T-shirts in the 1980s?

9 In 1985 which designer loaned Bruce Springsteen and his then wife, Julianne, his Lake Como villa for their honeymoon?

10 Who was the most famous recipient of a David and Elizabeth Emanuel creation?

11 What do the initials DKNY stand for?

12 Which fashion model has appeared in advertisements for Citroën cars?

13 Born in Hamburg in 1938, which former design director at Chanel is best known for his sophisticated day and evening wear?

14 In which year were nylon stockings introduced?

15 Which British designer was appointed dressmaker to the royal family in 1938?

16 Whose work has included sweatshirts trimmed with lace and satin, and shoes with upside-down Eiffel Towers as heels?

17 Which family firm started in the north of Italy in 1960, specialising in inexpensive yet fashionable knitwear?

18 Who is most associated with the concept of 'designer' jeans?

19 Who wrote the book *Men Without Ties*?

20 Which American president popularised the Panama hat?

19

21 Which Italian designer, born in 1890, liked to shock and amuse with her creations, which included hats in the shapes of ice cream cones and lamb cutlets?

22 Which French ex-tennis player was known as 'Le Crocodile' because of his aggressive style of play, which led to the crocodile being used as an emblem on his sportswear?

23 What nationality is designer Issey Miyake?

24 In which year did Levi Strauss take out a patent on his denim workpants?

25 Who directed the movie *Prêt à Porter*?

ANSWERS TO QUIZ 3

Children
1 English Civil War
2 Juliet
3 (First) Cousin
4 Three
5 Edsel
6 Cleopatra
7 The Railway Children
8 François Duvalier
9 Hamnet
10 Frank Zappa
11 Bob Cratchit
12 Charlie Sheen & Emilio Estevez
13 Sylvia
14 Gepetto
15 *Bugsy Malone*
16 *Charlie and the Chocolate Factory*
17 Anastasia
18 Nigel Havers
19 Little Lord Fauntleroy
20 Sylvester Stallone
21 Aristotle Onassis
22 Billy J Kramer and The Dakotas
23 Mary, Queen of Scots
24 Winston Churchill
25 Little Jimmy Osmond

Films of Books
1 *The Age of Innocence*
2 *Valmont*
3 Francis Ford Coppola
4 *Dr Strangelove, or How I Learned to Stop Worrying and Love the Bomb*
5 1962
6 *Jaws*
7 *Apocalypse Now*
8 Orson Welles
9 *Emma*
10 James Caan
11 *Lolita*
12 *Double Indemnity*
13 *Psycho*
14 Richard Burton
15 *The Shape of Things to Come*
16 *Carrie*
17 *Blade Runner*
18 They have all directed films of Charles Dickens novels
19 They were from books by the same author, Pierre Boulle
20 *Jackie Brown*
21 *Moby Dick*
22 *The Man in the Iron Mask*
23 *To Kill a Mockingbird*
24 *2001: A Space Odyssey*
25 *From Here to Eternity*

The Weather
1 An isotherm
2 The eye
3 A device for measuring wind speed
4 Chinook
5 Chlorofluorocarbons
6 Nitrogen, 78.08%
7 The Sahara
8 Fork lightning
9 Mares' tails
10 A cold front
11 The stratosphere
12 Equinox
13 The Roaring Forties
14 Mackerel sky
15 El Niño
16 Swedish
17 A depression – also called a low or a cyclone
18 Monsoon season
19 Ozone
20 74 mph
21 Thunder
22 A heatwave
23 Between five and ten miles
24 Permafrost
25 Minus forty degrees

Country & Western
1 Roy Rogers
2 Dolly Parton
3 Thirteen
4 The Mavericks
5 Vince Gill
6 Joe Walsh
7 Patsy Cline
8 Johnny Cash
9 Alison Krauss
10 Glen Campbell
11 Hank Williams
12 Don Gibson
13 Dixie Chicks
14 Garth Brooks
15 Lyle Lovett
16 Chet Atkins
17 Crystal Gayle
18 The banjo
19 Faron Young
20 Mike Nesmith
21 George Jones and Tammy Wynette
22 Steve Earle
23 Bobbie Gentry
24 Willie Nelson
25 Gram Parsons

Technology
1 Virtual reality
2 Bar codes
3 Fokker
4 The silicon chip
5 England
6 Photocopying
7 Britain
8 1930s (1932)
9 Philips
10 PVC
11 8 inches
12 Germany
13 Video home system
14 The electric toaster
15 Stereophonic sound
16 Buckminster Fuller
17 Velcro
18 1905
19 1903
20 1984
21 3M
22 The microwave oven
23 Black & Decker
24 Rotary internal combustion engine
25 The dial telephone

European Football
1 Atlético Madrid
2 Ronald
3 Bayern Munich
4 AC Milan
5 Kevin Keegan
6 Yugoslavia
7 Graeme Souness
8 Barcelona
9 Portugal
10 Star
11 Rosenborg BK
12 6-3
13 Philips
14 Croatia Zagreb
15 Juventus
16 Benfica
17 Diego Maradona
18 The Slovakian
19 Teddy Sheringham and Steve McManaman
20 Moscow
21 Luis Figo
22 Paris Saint-Germain
23 Red Star Belgrade
24 Belgian
25 Juventus

Police Shows
1 David Caruso
2 Jeremy Brett
3 *Hawaii Five-O*
4 *Endeavour*
5 Mike Post
6 Fred Gwynne and Al Lewis
7 *Hill Street Blues*
8 Telly Savalas's brother George
9 David Soul
10 Burt Reynolds
11 *The Princess Bride*
12 *The Streets of San Francisco*
13 *Cop Rock*
14 *CHiPs*
15 *The Untouchables*
16 *Hawaii Five-O*
17 Hawaii
18 Regan and Carter in *The Sweeney*
19 *Fiddler on the Roof*
20 The right eye
21 Loretta Swit
22 Chief Robert T Ironside
23 *Moonlighting*
24 Carroll O'Connor
25 *Police Squad*

Fashion
1 The Duke of Windsor
2 Mary Quant
3 Coco Chanel
4 1975
5 Hardy Amies
6 Christian Dior
7 Vivienne Westwood
8 Katharine Hamnett
9 Gianni Versace
10 Lady Diana Spencer
11 Donna Karan New York
12 Claudia Schiffer
13 Karl Lagerfeld
14 1940
15 Norman Hartnell
16 Jean-Paul Gaultier
17 Benetton
18 Calvin Klein
19 Gianni Versace
20 Theodore Roosevelt
21 Elsa Schiaparelli
22 René Lacoste
23 Japanese
24 1872
25 Robert Altman

THE GREATEST TRIVIA QUIZ BOOK

QUIZ 4

1 Which former prime minister of France became his country's president after the resignation of Charles de Gaulle?

2 Which politician enrolled in the law faculty of Havana University in 1945, at the age of nineteen?

3 Who was Russian president after Yuri Andropov and before Mikhail Gorbachev?

4 Who caused uproar in Britain in 1968 with his 'rivers of blood' speech on the immigration issue?

5 Which American chaired the Good Friday agreement in Ireland in 1998?

6 Who was deemed to have made a breach of protocol when he touched the Queen's arm during a visit to Australia?

7 Which English prime minister took over leadership of the party in February 1975?

8 Who replaced Ehud Barak as Israel's prime minister in early 2001?

9 Who was Bertie Aherne's predecessor as Prime Minister of Ireland?

10 Which communist leader, who died in 1969, once worked as a pastry cook in London?

11 Who was replaced by Peter Mandelson as Secretary of State for Northern Ireland in 1999?

12 Which Russian president famously banged his shoe on the table while Harold Macmillan was speaking to the United Nations in 1960?

13 In which year was Mikhail Gorbachev awarded the Nobel Peace Prize?

14 Who became the first British Labour Prime Minister in 1924?

15 How did President Sadat of Egypt die in 1981?

16 Which German Chancellor resigned in May 1974 after a spy was discovered working in his office?

17 In 1967, forty-one-year-old Svetlana Alliluyeva defected from the Soviet Union. Who was her father?

18 Which Democratic candidate ran against Ronald Reagan in the 1984 US election?

19 Who became British Prime Minister in 1783 in his twenty-fifth year?

20 Which future French President lost the 1974 election to Valéry Giscard d'Estaing?

21 Who is the leader of the SDLP in Northern Ireland?

22 Which former British Prime Minister died in 1986 at the age of 92?

23 Which two Middle East leaders shared the 1978 Nobel Peace Prize?

24 Which British politician of the 1970s disappeared in Miami, Florida, leaving clothes on the beach, and reappeared in Australia?

25 Who was British Prime Minister during the Suez crisis in 1956?

1 What is Michael Caine's real name?

2 In which 1988 comedy did Caine and Ben Kingsley play Sherlock Holmes and Dr Watson respectively?

3 In which Peter Sellers film did Caine appear in 1962?

4 Who starred with Caine in the 1982 thriller *Deathtrap*, playing a young playwright who Caine's character intends to murder?

5 In which Len Deighton story did Caine first star as agent Harry Palmer in 1965?

6 For which film did he receive his first Academy Award as supporting actor?

7 With which other young British actor did Caine share an apartment in London in the 1960s?

8 Apart from starring in the 1987 film of Frederick Forsyth's *The Fourth Protocol*, what was Caine's other involvement in the film?

9 Why did he choose the surname Caine?

10 In which year was *Educating Rita* released?

11 In which film did Caine play Dr Wilbur Larch, in a performance that gained him a second Academy Award?

12 Who starred alongside Caine in the 1988 film *Dirty Rotten Scoundrels*?

13 Which British actress won an Oscar for her role as Caine's wife in the 1978 comedy *California Suite*?

14 Which American actress starred with Caine in *Alfie*?

15 What significant event in Caine's life took place on 16 June 2000?

16 In which 1988 film did he play a sleazy talent agent who meets an agoraphobic young woman with a brilliant talent for singing?

17 Caine played a villain in *Mona Lisa* opposite which other leading British actor?

18 What was the title of the 1980 Brian De Palma murder thriller in which Caine starred as psychiatrist Dr Robert Elliott?

19 Which 1971 gangster film was based on Ted Lewis's novel *Jack's Return Home*, about a man going up to Newcastle to investigate his brother's death?

20 Which 1964 film is generally regarded as the film that made Caine a star?

21 Who co-starred with Caine in the 1972 thriller comedy *Sleuth*?

22 Which flamboyant British director was at the helm of Caine's third film as Harry Palmer, *Billion Dollar Brain*?

23 Which film, based on a Kipling short story, was directed by John Huston who, decades after wanting to make the film with Humphrey Bogart and Clark Gable, finally made it in 1975 with Caine and Sean Connery?

24 In 1997 Caine played support in the film *Blood and Wine*, as an ex-con. Who played the lead role in that film?

25 Michael Caine has long been known as a trivia fan. What phrase of his became popular as a result?

1 Which water bird has brown and black feathers with a white flank slash and a red beak shield?

2 Which bird is renowned for taking over the nests of other species?

3 Which bird is resident of the American Southwest and has been immortalised in a cartoon series?

4 What colour are the eggs of the redstart?

5 What colour is the beak of a mature mute swan?

6 Which continent is the natural habitat of the ostrich?

7 For how long does a female turkey incubate her eggs?

8 What is meant by a low wing bearing?

9 Which bird, sometimes called the peewit, has dark green plumage with white neck and underside, and a distinctive green crest?

10 Which curved-billed bird is the largest European wader?

11 Which has a black bill, the crow or the rook?

12 Which bird was depicted on the rear of the farthing coin?

13 Which is the smallest of all birds?

14 What type of bird is a teal?

15 How many are in a clutch of blackbird's eggs?

16 Which is the largest species of penguin?

17 To which family does the jay belong?

18 Where do swallows go when they migrate from Britain for the winter?

19 Which bird is the emblem of the United States?

20 Which bird of prey can often be seen hovering above hedges and ditches at the roadside?

21 Native to America, what type of bird are Lewis's red-bellied, ladder-backed and Nuttall's?

22 Which seabird has a black and white body and a very large, bright yellow and red beak?

23 Which is the largest owl found in Britain?

24 Which lays blue eggs, the song thrush or the mistle thrush?

25 Which country is the natural habitat of the emu?

18

1 Which Patti Smith album featured a cover shot by controversial photographer Robert Mapplethorpe?

2 Born James Osterburg, who is called the 'Godfather of Punk'?

3 According to the title of their 1979 hit, where did The Leyton Buzzards spend Saturday Night?

4 With which band was David Johansen lead singer?

5 By what name did Marion Elliott become famous, fronting the band X-Ray Spex?

6 Which legendary New York punk club saw appearances by the Ramones, Television and Blondie, among others?

7 Who did Sid Vicious replace in the Sex Pistols?

8 Which ex-member of Television fronted the Voidoids?

9 What is Johnny Rotten's real name?

10 Who had a hit in 1977 with 'Roadrunner'?

11 Whose 1979 debut album was called *Inflammable Material*?

12 Who did the Stilettoes go on to become?

13 Which American band comprised Jeffrey Hyman, John Cummings, Douglas Colvin, and Tommy Erdelyi, although all were known professionally by the same surname?

14 Which member of The Velvet Underground produced Patti Smith's debut album, *Horses*?

15 By what archetypal punk name was drummer Chris Miller known?

16 Which famous fashion designer was co-owner of Malcolm McLaren's Sex clothes shop in London's Kings Road?

17 On which label was the Sex Pistols' first single, 'Anarchy in the UK'?

18 With which mod revival band did Style Council's Mick Talbot play keyboards?

19 By what name is John Graham Mellor, born in Ankara, Turkey in 1952, better known?

20 Which member of the Buzzcocks went on to form the band Magazine?

21 Who sang with the Attractions?

22 Which product was advertised using The Clash's 'Should I Stay Or Should I Go', making the record a UK number one hit in 1991?

23 Which American band had their biggest UK success with a spiky version of The Rolling Stones' 'Satisfaction'?

24 Whose albums included *Plastic Letters* and *Parallel Lines*?

25 Which band featured ex-New York Dolls guitarist Johnny Thunders?

1 Which scandal was uncovered by journalists Bob Woodward and Carl Bernstein?

2 Which Hollywood actor was charged with, and acquitted of, three rape charges in 1943?

3 Which rock & roll singer shocked Britain in 1958 when he arrived with his thirteen-year-old wife?

4 In which year did King Edward VIII abdicate from the English throne?

5 Which entertainer sued the *Daily Mirror* in 1959 for publishing an article implying that he was a homosexual?

6 Who was the Queen's art adviser exposed in November 1979 as a spy for the Russians?

7 Who was prime minister during the Profumo scandal?

8 Which titled lady was pictured in a compromising position with a 'headless' man?

9 Which Conservative MP admitted in 1983 to having an affair with his secretary, Sara Keays, who went on to have his child?

10 With which pop star do you associate allegations involving a child named Jordan Chandler?

11 What was the name of the Arkansas property development with which the Clintons were involved?

12 Which star of the silent screen was accused of the rape and manslaughter of actress Virginia Rappe in 1920?

13 Germans Konrad Kujau and Gerd Heidemann were arrested in May 1983 for their part in which fraudulent publication?

14 In which year did National Guardsmen open fire on student demonstrators at Kent State University, Ohio, killing four?

15 In which year did Palestinian terrorists kill members of the Israeli Olympic team?

16 Who was sentenced to ten days in prison and fined $500 for 'indecent behaviour' on the Broadway stage in 1927?

17 What rank was Oliver North at the time of the 'Irangate' hearing?

18 Nick Leeson was held responsible for the fall of which merchant bank in 1995?

19 Which American TV evangelist was involved in a sex and money scandal in 1987?

20 Which skater allegedly had rival Nancy Kerrigan attacked at the 1994 Winter Olympics?

21 The subject of a Robert Redford film, what was the name of the 1950s American TV quiz show in which Charles Van Doren received questions in advance to keep his winning run going?

22 In which year was hostage-turned-terrorist Patti Hearst arrested by FBI agents?

23 Who wrote a report on the misconduct of President Clinton in the wake of the Monica Lewinsky affair?

24 What was the name given to the scandal involving disc jockeys or radio stations being bribed to play certain records?

25 Which South African township saw riots in 1976 that resulted in 175 deaths?

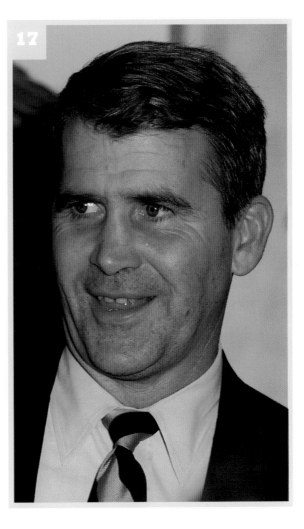

1 Where did Roger Bannister run the first sub-four-minute mile in 1954?

2 How long did Bannister's time of 3m 59.4sec stand as a world record?

3 Which future women's 10,000 metre world record holder first represented the USA at the age of fourteen?

4 Who was the first man to jump eight feet in the high jump?

5 Which American discus thrower won four consecutive Olympic titles in addition to being a four-time world record holder?

6 Jesse Owens set the record for the long jump in 1935 with 8.13m. Who finally bettered his distance in 1960?

7 Florence Griffith-Joyner broke the 200 metres world record in the semifinals at the Seoul Olympics on 29 September 1988. What happened less than two hours later?

8 Which three British athletes broke the mile and 1,500 metres records a total of eleven times between 1979 and 1985?

9 After dominating the 400 metres for so long, who finally broke Harry 'Butch' Reynolds' 1988 world record in 1999?

10 In which event did Christos Papanikolau become the first Greek to set an athletics world record in 1970?

11 In the final at which world championships did Sally Gunnell break the 400 metres hurdles world record?

6

12 Moses Kiptanui of Kenya broke the 3,000 metres steeplechase world record twice in Zurich, in 1992 and 1995. What was remarkable about the second occasion?

13 Jumping eighteen metres for the first time, who broke the men's triple jump world record twice in the same competition at the 1995 world championships?

14 Which Polish athlete was the first woman to break the fifty-second barrier for the 400 metres in 1974?

15 Why was German Klaus Tafelmeier's 1986 javelin world record nineteen metres shorter than the previous record throw?

16 Whose outlawed time of 9.79 seconds for the 100 metres did American Maurice Greene equal when he set the world record in Athens in 1999?

17 What nationality was Chi Cheng, who set world records for the women's 100 metres, 200 metres and 100 metres hurdles in 1970?

18 At which Olympics did Daley Thompson set his fourth and final world record in the decathlon?

19 Which city's marathon was won by Norwegian Greta Weitz nine times in total?

20 Which Finnish distance runner held the 5,000 and 10,000 metres world records and also won both events in the 1972 and 1976 Olympic games?

21 Kenyan-born Wilson Kipketer finally beat Sebastian Coe's 1981 time for the 800 metres in 1997. Which country does he now represent?

22 Which Ukrainian athlete has held and improved the pole vault world record since 1984?

11

23 Which heptathlete won two Olympic and two world titles in addition to breaking the world record four times between 1986 and 1988?

24 How many times did Romanian Iolanda Balas break the women's high jump world record between 1956 and 1961?

25 Which 400-metre hurdler, a four-time world record holder, won 122 consecutive races between 1977 and 1987?

1 Which educational programme, first shown in the 1960s, was the creation of Television Workshop co-founder Joan Ganz Cooney?

2 Former Mr Universe Lou Ferrigno played TV's the Incredible Hulk, but who played his alter ego, mild-mannered scientist Bruce Banner?

3 Which cartoon series, starring a drawling dog, was the first to win an Emmy for Outstanding Achievement in Children's Programming?

4 Hong Kong Phooey's cases were usually solved by his accomplice, whose efforts were never recognised. What was his name?

5 What was the Littlest Hobo's name?

6 Taking its cue from *The Flintstones*, which 1960s cartoon series featured a suburban US family of the late 21st century?

7 Where did the Hair Bear Bunch live?

8 What was Mike Judge's animated follow-up to *Beavis and Butthead*?

9 *Gilligan's Island* star Alan Hale Jr appeared as an heroic train driver in which 1950s TV series?

10 Which character played the drums in the Muppets band?

11 Which cartoon series revolved around the antics of the inhabitants of Jellystone National Park?

12 Francine Pascal's novels, set in a Californian high school, became a popular 1990s TV series. What was it called?

13 What is the name of the *South Park* character who is regularly killed?

14 What kind of animals are Rocky and Bullwinkle?

15 Who did the voices of Batman and Robin in the 1970s cartoon series called *The New Adventures of Batman*?

16 What kind of animal was My Friend Flicka?

17 TV's McCloud, Dennis Weaver, played the part of a game warden in a 1960s series about a bear cub. What was it called?

18 The Flintstones' daughter and the Rubbles' adopted son became inseparable. What were their names?

19 Which famous pop star narrated *Thomas the Tank Engine*?

20 What does 'Daktari' mean?

21 George Dolenz played TV's The Count of Monte Cristo. His son became a TV star himself in the 1960s. In which TV programme?

22 What was the name of Rin Tin Tin's eleven-year-old master?

23 Who played Robin Hood in the 1950s TV series?

24 What was the name of Champion the Wonder Horse's German shepherd dog companion?

25 Which myopic cartoon character had two nephews called Prezley and Waldo?

1 What is the origin of the word 'biscuit'?

2 The Greek words for 'beautiful', 'appearance' and 'I behold' converge to give us which word?

3 What was the name of the Swiss physician who induced a trance-like state in his patients, a condition which now bears his name?

4 Which word, a mixture of Norse and Anglo-Saxon, means son of, or belonging to, a creek or inlet?

5 Which pasta dish has a name that means 'little worms'?

6 The Arabic expression 'shah mat' signifies 'the king is dead'. How do we know this expression in relation to a popular game?

7 Which term is used to describe words such as 'chit-chat', 'helter-skelter' and 'tittle-tattle'?

8 Which word originated at Eton boys' school, as a result of the shortness of the school jackets?

9 Which word, meaning guilty, has passed out of common usage, although its opposite is still in everyday use?

10 Which type of hat takes its name from the Prussian town in which it was originally made?

11 Which mode of transport gets its name from the old Dutch 'jachtim', meaning to speed or to hunt?

12 Which drink gets its name from Jerez in Spain?

13 Where does the word 'ginormous' come from?

14 The name of which political party translates as 'we ourselves'?

15 Which type of transport got its name during the Second World War because it was used as a general purpose vehicle?

16 To which writer does the word 'Shavian' apply?

17 Which word, describing unintelligible talk, is derived from the sound made by a turkey?

18 Which musical instrument got its name from the Latin for 'soft' and 'loud'?

19 Which record label got its name because it was based in Detroit, an important centre of the automobile industry?

20 The Romans paid their soldiers *salarium*, or 'salt money'. Which word do we get from this?

21 What is the meaning of the word 'rabbi'?

22 Which expression, meaning to be in financial straits, comes from the practice of tradesmen marking 'query' against the name of a customer who couldn't pay?

23 Which adjective do we get from the Latin 'punctum', meaning 'point'?

24 Which ancient country was named from the Greek 'mesos' and 'potamos' because it lay between two rivers?

25 What contraction of the word 'grandfather' is used as a slang term to describe someone in charge?

ANSWERS TO QUIZ 4

Politicians
1 Georges Pompidou
2 Fidel Castro
3 Konstantin Chernenko
4 Enoch Powell
5 Senator George Mitchell
6 Paul Keating
7 Margaret Thatcher
8 Ariel Sharon
9 John Bruton
10 Ho Chi Minh
11 Mo Mowlam
12 Nikita Krushchev
13 1990
14 Ramsay MacDonald
15 He was shot during a military parade
16 Willy Brandt
17 Joseph Stalin
18 Walter Mondale
19 William Pitt the Younger
20 François Mitterrand
21 John Hume
22 Harold Macmillan
23 Anwar Sadat and Menachem Begin
24 John Stonehouse
25 Anthony Eden

Michael Caine
1 Maurice Micklewhite
2 *Without a Clue*
3 *The Wrong Arm of the Law*
4 Christopher Reeve
5 *The Ipcress File*
6 *Hannah and her Sisters*
7 Terence Stamp
8 He was executive producer
9 After his favourite movie, *The Caine Mutiny*
10 1983
11 *The Cider House Rules*
12 Steve Martin
13 Maggie Smith
14 Shelley Winters
15 He was knighted
16 *Little Voice*
17 Bob Hoskins
18 *Dressed to Kill*
19 *Get Carter*
20 *Zulu*
21 Lawrence Olivier
22 Ken Russell
23 *The Man Who Would be King*
24 Jack Nicholson
25 'Not a lot of people know that'

Birds
1 Moorhen
2 Cuckoo
3 Roadrunner
4 Usually blue with a greenish tinge
5 Orange
6 Africa
7 Approximately 28 days
8 A low body weight to wing area ratio
9 The lapwing
10 Curlew
11 Crow
12 Wren
13 Bee hummingbird, weighing 2 grams
14 Duck
15 Usually between 3 and 5
16 Emperor
17 Crow
18 South Africa
19 Bald eagle
20 Kestrel
21 Woodpeckers
22 Atlantic puffin
23 Snowy owl
24 Song thrush
25 Australia

Punk Rock
1 *Horses*
2 Iggy Pop
3 Beneath The Plastic Palm Trees
4 The New York Dolls
5 Poly Styrene
6 CBGBs
7 Glen Matlock
8 Richard Hell
9 John Lydon
10 Jonathan Richman and the Modern Lovers
11 Stiff Little Fingers
12 Blondie
13 The Ramones
14 John Cale
15 Rat Scabies
16 Vivienne Westwood
17 EMI
18 The Merton Parkas
19 Joe Strummer
20 Howard Devoto
21 Elvis Costello
22 Levi's
23 Devo
24 Blondie
25 The Heartbreakers

Scandals
1 Watergate
2 Errol Flynn
3 Jerry Lee Lewis
4 1936
5 Liberace
6 Sir Anthony Blunt
7 Harold Macmillan
8 The Duchess of Argyll
9 Cecil Parkinson
10 Michael Jackson
11 Whitewater
12 'Fatty' Arbuckle
13 The Hitler Diaries
14 1970
15 1972
16 Mae West
17 Lieutenant Colonel
18 Barings
19 Jim Bakker
20 Tonya Harding
21 *Twenty-One*
22 1975
23 Kenneth Starr
24 Payola
25 Soweto

Athletics Records
1 Oxford
2 46 days
3 Mary Decker
4 Javier Sotomayor, Cuba
5 Al Oerter
6 Ralph Boston, USA
7 She broke it again
8 Sebastian Coe, Steve Ovett & Steve Cram
9 Michael Johnson, USA
10 Pole vault (he was also first over 18 feet)
11 Stuttgart, 1983
12 He broke the eight-minute barrier
13 Jonathan Edwards, GB
14 Irena Szewinska
15 The specification of the javelin was altered
16 Canadian Ben Johnson's
17 Taiwanese
18 Los Angeles, 1984
19 New York
20 Lasse Viren
21 Denmark
22 Sergey Bubka
23 Jackie Joyner-Kersee, USA
24 Fourteen
25 Soweto

Children's TV
1 *Sesame Street*
2 Bill Bixby
3 *Huckleberry Hound*
4 Spot the cat
5 London
6 *The Jetsons*
7 Wonderland Zoo
8 *King of the Hill*
9 Casey Jones
10 Animal
11 *Yogi Bear*
12 *Sweet Valley High*
13 Kenny
14 A flying squirrel and a moose
15 Adam West and Burt Ward
16 A black stallion
17 *Gentle Ben*
18 Pebbles and Bam-Bam
19 Ringo Starr
20 Doctor, in Swahili
21 *The Monkees*
22 Rusty
23 Richard Green
24 Rebel
25 Mister Magoo

Words & Names
1 From the French 'bis' (twice) and 'cuit' (cooked)
2 Kaleidoscope (kalos, eidos, scopeo)
3 Franz Mesmer
4 Viking
5 Vermicelli
6 Checkmate
7 Ricochet, or reduplicated words
8 Bumfreezer
9 Nocent
10 Homburg
11 Yacht
12 Sherry
13 A blend of gigantic and enormous
14 Sinn Fein
15 Jeep (GP – general purpose)
16 George Bernard Shaw
17 Gobbledegook
18 Pianoforte
19 Motown
20 Salary
21 My teacher
22 Queer Street
23 Punctual
24 Mesopotamia
25 Gaffer

THE GREATEST TRIVIA QUIZ BOOK

QUIZ 5

1 Who is the narrator of *Moby Dick*?

2 What nationality was James Bond's mother?

3 What was Sidney Carton's profession in *A Tale of Two Cities*?

4 'Scud' East was the eponymous hero's friend in which famous 19th-century novel?

5 Who was the central character in Oscar Wilde's only novel?

6 What were the Christian names of Dr Jekyll and Mr Hyde?

7 Who did Sherlock Holmes call *the* woman?

8 Which surname is common to the central characters of *Kim* and *Gone With the Wind*?

9 What is the Christian name of P G Wodehouse's famous gentleman's gentleman?

10 How are Marco and Giuseppe Palmieri better known?

11 Who created Sam Spade?

12 Who was known as Trusty Scout to his constant companion?

13 How is Jack Dawkins better known in a Dickens novel?

14 Which famous novel features the Starkadder family?

15 In the world of TV soap operas what was the claim to fame of Kristin Shephard?

16 What is the name of the one-legged sea cook in *Treasure Island*?

11

17 In which famous novel does the character Major Major Major appear?

18 Lara Antipova is a central character in which famous novel and movie?

19 Who created the detective Lew Archer?

20 Vlad V of Wallachia (Vlad the Impaler) was the inspiration for which notorious character?

21 In which children's book would you encounter the Oompa Loompas?

22 Virgil Tibbs was the central character of which famous movie?

23 Who created Brer Rabbit?

24 In which Shakespearean comedy does Malvolio appear?

25 Who was the gypsy girl loved by Quasimodo?

1 In which musical would you hear the song 'Something Good'?

2 Which musical won the best picture Oscar in 1968?

3 Who wrote the lyrics to the songs in *West Side Story*?

4 For which film was director Bob Fosse awarded an Oscar in 1972?

5 In which musical was there a dance routine set at a barn raising?

6 In which musical did Donald O'Connor perform the breathtaking 'Make 'em Laugh' routine?

7 Which of the Gold Diggers movies contains the song 'We're in the Money'?

8 Where was the setting for *On the Town*?

9 On which Shakespeare play was *Kiss Me Kate* based?

10 Who directed *A Chorus Line*?

11 In which film did Doris Day sing the Oscar-winning song 'Secret Love'?

12 Who played the lead role in the screen adaptation of Dennis Potter's *Pennies from Heaven*?

13 In which film did Fred Astaire and Ginger Rogers first team up?

14 In the song 'Oh, What a Beautiful Mornin'' from *Oklahoma*, how high does the corn grow?

15 Why does Gene Kelly suddenly stop in the 'Singin' in the Rain' routine?

16 Which big-voiced singer is usually associated with the Irving Berlin song 'There's No Business like Show Business'?

17 In which musical does the song 'Old Man River' feature?

18 Who played Anna in the 1956 film *The King and I*?

19 In which musical did Clint Eastwood perform 'I Talk to the Trees'?

20 The soundtrack to which musical topped the UK album charts for seventy consecutive weeks between 1958 and 1960?

21 Which sixties model starred in Ken Russell's film of the musical *The Boyfriend*?

22 Who won an Oscar for his portrayal of Broadway legend George M Cohan in *Yankee Doodle Dandy*?

23 In addition to co-directing *West Side Story* with Robert Wise, what was Jerome Robbins's other contribution to the film?

24 Who starred as Cole Porter in the 1944 film *Night and Day*?

25 What was the tile of the 1956 musical remake of *The Philadelphia Story* ?

23

1 The two stars to the right of the Plough, in the constellation of Ursa Major, are called the Pointers. To what do they point?

2 Sharing its name with an Arnold Schwarzenegger film, what name is given to the line dividing the light and dark portions of the moon?

3 On which planet is the *Valles Marineris* chasm?

4 Approximately how long does it take the sun's light to reach Earth?

5 Why is Pluto not in Gustav Holst's music suite *The Planets*?

6 What is the name of the largest moon in the solar system?

7 In which year was Comet Hale-Bopp last visible?

8 In 1995 the star 51 Pegasi was the first star to be confirmed as having what?

9 Which planet was discovered in 1781 by amateur astronomer William Hershel, working at his home in Bath, England?

10 How many years does it take for Neptune to orbit the sun?

25

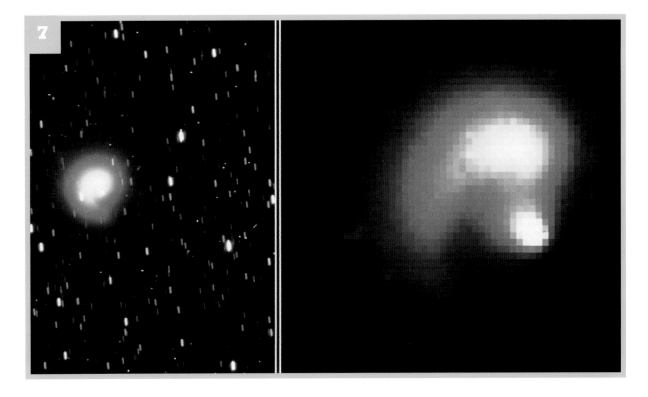

7

11 Who made the discovery that the sun spins?

12 Which constellation has three stars that appear to be in a straight line, and that are referred to as a belt?

13 Where are the Epsilon Peak, the crater Copernicus and the Straight Wall?

14 Which is the only star in our solar system?

15 The northern lights are called the *aurora borealis*. What are the southern lights known as?

16 Io is the most volcanically active body in the solar system. Which planet does it orbit?

17 By what nickname is the star Sirius known?

18 What was discovered by Clyde Tombaugh from the Lowell Observatory, Arizona, in 1930?

19 How many moons are there in our solar system: a) 41 b) 51 or c) 61?

20 Which planet spins on a near-horizontal axis, as opposed to vertical or near-vertical?

21 In which constellation are the stars Castor and Pollux?

22 During which event can you witness a phenomenon nicknamed the 'diamond ring'?

23 Why is Neptune sometimes the farthest planet from the sun?

24 Are sunspots the hottest or coolest regions of the sun's surface?

25 Which planet in the solar system is nearest in size to Earth?

11

1 What is Madonna's surname?

2 Which instrument did she play in the band the Breakfast Club?

3 When is Madonna's birthday?

4 To which record label did Madonna first sign?

5 What was Madonna's first UK number one single?

6 In which film did Madonna play her first significant role?

7 Which other actress also starred in that film?

8 What is the name of Madonna's second child?

9 Madonna first met Sean Penn in 1985 during the shooting of which single's video?

10 What is Madonna's nickname for her daughter Lourdes Maria?

11 Who directed Madonna in the 1996 film *Evita*?

12 What was the location for Madonna and Sean Penn's wedding in 1985?

13 Which track from the *True Blue* album was used in Sean Penn's film *At Close Range*?

14 Who starred opposite Madonna in the film *Dick Tracy*?

15 Which outrageous fashion designer was responsible for Madonna's pointed brassières?

16 In which film did Madonna and Sean Penn star together?

17 What is the name of Madonna's own record label?

18 Who is Lourdes's father?

19 In which film was Madonna less than complimentary about Kevin Costner?

20 With which company did Madonna sign a $60 million deal in 1992?

21 Who played Che Guevara opposite Madonna in the film *Evita*?

22 From which album was the single 'Papa Don't Preach' taken?

23 What is Madonna's shoe size?

24 Which British comic character appeared in the video for Madonna's single 'Music'?

25 Who produced the singles 'Holiday' and 'Crazy For You'?

15

9

6 Which novel, published in 1932, was a vision of the future as a sanitised society?

7 To what position was John Masefield appointed in May 1930?

8 In 1939 which pub game was banned in Glasgow for being 'too dangerous'?

9 Which great American inventor died in October 1931?

10 Which Australian cricketer, playing for New South Wales against Queensland, scored a then world record first-class innings of 452 not out?

11 Which two European leaders signed a non-aggression pact on 23 August 1939?

12 What was the name of the vehicle in which Sir Malcolm Campbell broke the 300 mph barrier in 1935?

13 Which vehicle, designed by Ferdinand Porsche, went into mass production in 1936?

14 Which type of vegetable went on sale in frozen form in Massachusetts in June 1930?

15 What was the name of the man who pioneered the above method of freezing food?

16 Which American gangster was shot dead outside a Chicago cinema in July 1934?

17 Which black athlete's successes at the 1936 Berlin Olympics caused Hitler to storm out of the stadium?

18 What was the maiden name of Wallis Simpson, for whom Edward VIII abdicated in 1936?

1 What came to an end in the United States in December 1933?

2 Of which country did Robert Menzies become prime minister in April 1939?

3 Which great ocean liner was launched in 1934?

4 Which London building was gutted by fire in November 1936?

5 Which woman flew from England to Australia in 1930?

19 On 1 May 1931 the world's then tallest building was opened in New York City. Which building was it?

20 Which Margaret Mitchell novel, later a successful film, won the 1937 Pulitzer Prize?

21 Which former Labour MP formed the New Party in February 1931?

22 Whose radio production of *War of the Worlds* caused widespread panic in America in 1938?

23 Which corporation opened its new headquarters in Portland Place, London, in May 1932?

24 What type of natural disaster hit the American Midwest in 1935?

25 Composer George Gershwin died in 1937 at the age of thirty-eight. How did he die?

19

1 What are the four Grand Slam events?

2 Which player won her last Grand Slam tournament in Paris in 1999?

3 Who was the first Russian player to win a Grand Slam event when he won the French title in 1996?

4 Which player was stabbed in the back at a tournament in Hamburg in 1993?

5 Although she represents Switzerland, in which country was Martina Hingis born?

6 Which event was won by Miroslav Mecir in 1988, Marc Rosset in 1992, Andre Agassi in 1996 and Yevgeny Kafelnikov in 2000?

7 Between the years 1978 and 1984 which two men dominated the US Open singles title?

8 When Billie-Jean King won the first open Wimbledon in 1968, what was her prize money?

9 Who was the beaten finalist in the Wimbledon men's singles in 1992, 1994 and 1998?

10 What was unusual about the 1986 Australian Open?

11 Which American woman was never beaten at Wimbledon, winning three consecutive titles in the 1950s before retiring after a riding accident?

12 Before Venus Williams won at Wimbledon in 2000, which of the Grand Slam tournaments had her younger sister Serena won?

13 Who won the US Open men's title in 1990 at the age of nineteen?

14 Who won her first Wimbledon title, the women's doubles with Helena Sukova, in 1996 at the age of 15?

15 What is the only score at which a player can serve from the right-hand side of the court to win a game?

16 The new main court for the US Open, opened in 1997, is named in memory of which American player?

17 Which British TV presenter won the women's singles title at the 1976 French Open?

18 Which player topped the women's rankings for a record 377 weeks, including a run of 186 weeks between 1987 and 1991?

19 Between 1974 and 1981, which man won six French titles, five Wimbledons, and was runner-up four times in the US?

20 How often are the balls changed in tennis tournaments?

21 Which woman won the US singles title in 1968, the Australian in 1972, and Wimbledon in 1977?

22 In which year did Greg Rusedski opt to play for Great Britain instead of Canada?

23 At the time of writing, who is the last man to have beaten Pete Sampras at Wimbledon?

24 In Grand Slam events, what do these numbers mean: winner 520; runner-up 364; semifinalist 234; quarterfinalist 130?

25 Which Australian woman won all four Grand Slam titles in 1970?

1 On whose show did The Beatles make their US television debut?

2 Which US TV presenter starred in *The Color Purple*?

3 Which famous British broadcaster, who died in 1965, has two broadcasting sons called Jonathan and David?

4 Which disc jockey played himself in George Lucas's film *American Graffiti*?

5 Which American newsman broke the news of President Kennedy's death to the nation?

6 Which famous rock and roll disc jockey fell from grace during the Payola scandal of the late 1950s?

7 Which London-born presenter, a familiar face to US and UK television audiences, was once mayor of Cincinnati?

8 Which celebrated broadcaster presents 'Letter from America' on BBC Radio 4 every week?

9 Which presenter/actress has her own production company called Harpo?

10 In which field are Connie Chung and Tom Brockaw known in the US?

11 Which fashion designer once co-hosted *Eurotrash* with Antoine de Caunes?

12 Which American show is hosted by Jay Leno?

13 Which US disc jockey was nicknamed 'The Fifth Beatle'?

14 Which film director appeared in a series in the fifties and sixties in which he introduced tales of suspense?

15 Which American comedian hosts the talk show *Politically Incorrect*?

16 Arnold Schwarzenegger, Michael J. Fox and Tom Hanks have all served as presenters on which Sky mystery anthology?

17 Which actress-turned-chat-show-host made her name in the film *Hairspray*?

18 Which US comedy series is based around a talk show and stars Garry Shandling in the title role?

19 Which TV series featured the radio DJs Dr Johnny Fever and Venus Flytrap?

20 What were Rowan and Martin's first names?

21 Which American talk show presenter features top ten lists on his show?

22 Vic Perrin regularly intoned 'There is nothing wrong with your television set' at the start of which 1960s sci-fi series?

23 Which Australian presenter has made travel documentaries in various foreign locations, the programmes being called *A Postcard from ...*?

24 Which controversial radio presenter starred as himself in the film *Private Parts*?

25 Who was the resident DJ on KBHR radio in *Northern Exposure*?

1 Who was the androgyne offspring of Hermes and Aphrodite?

2 Which giant was made to carry the heavens on his shoulders as punishment for having fought against Zeus?

3 In which country's mythology is Yi the divine order?

4 Which huge, ferocious monster of Phoenician mythology is referred to in the Book of Isaiah as the 'crooked serpent'?

5 Who is the Egyptian god of the moon?

6 What name is given to the immense hall for the glorious dead in Norse mythology?

7 By what other names is the god Odin known?

8 Which creature had the head of a bull and the body of a man?

9 By which collective name are Clio, Euterpe, Thalia, Melpomene, Terpsichore, Erato, Polyhymnia, Urania, and Calliope known?

10 What is the Roman equivalent of the Greek god Poseidon?

11 Which serpent haunted the caves of Parnassus, whose name lives on in one of the world's largest snakes?

12 To which place was the mortally wounded Arthur ferried by three mysterious women in a black boat?

13 Which band of warriors was responsible for the safety of the High King of Ireland?

14 With Vishnu and Brahma, who is the third god of the Hindu Trimurti?

15 Who is the Egyptian sun god?

16 Who was the half-sister of King Arthur?

17 Who went into Hades to bring back his wife Eurydice?

18 What is the name given to Vishnu's incarnations on earth?

19 Who possessed a hammer called Mjollnir?

20 In which country was Zoroaster, or Zarathustra, a great religious reformer?

21 Who was the only knight of the round table to see the entire Grail?

22 What is the name given to an 'enlightened being' destined to become a buddha?

23 In Chinese mythology, which creature symbolises the male, yang element?

24 Which animal's form does the Egyptian goddess Bastet take?

25 Who sapped Merlin's power and bound him in stone?

ANSWERS TO QUIZ 5

Fictional Characters
1 Ishmael
2 Swiss
3 Barrister
4 *Tom Brown's Schooldays*
5 Dorian Gray
6 Henry (Jekyll), Edward (Hyde)
7 Irene Adler
8 O'Hara (Kimball and Scarlett)
9 Reginald
10 The Gondoliers
11 Dashiell Hammett
12 The Lone Ranger (Kemo Sabe)
13 The Artful Dodger
14 *Cold Comfort Farm*
15 She shot J R Ewing
16 Long John Silver
17 *Catch-22*
18 *Dr Zhivago*
19 Ross McDonald
20 Count Dracula
21 *Charlie and the Chocolate Factory*
22 *In the Heat of the Night*
23 Joel Chandler Harris
24 *Twelfth Night*
25 Esmeralda

Musicals
1 *The Sound of Music*
2 *Oliver!*
3 Stephen Sondheim
4 *Cabaret*
5 *Seven Brides for Seven Brothers*
6 *Singin' in the Rain*
7 *Gold Diggers of 1933*
8 New York
9 *The Taming of the Shrew*
10 Richard Attenborough
11 *Calamity Jane*
12 Steve Martin
13 *Flying Down to Rio*
14 As high as an elephant's eye
15 He notices the policeman
16 Ethel Merman
17 *Showboat*
18 Deborah Kerr
19 *Paint Your Wagon*
20 *South Pacific*
21 Twiggy
22 James Cagney
23 Choreography
24 Cary Grant
25 *High Society*

The Night Sky
1 Polaris, the Pole Star
2 The terminator
3 Mars

4 Eight minutes
5 The piece was written before Pluto's discovery
6 Ganymede
7 1997
8 An orbiting planet
9 Uranus
10 165
11 Galileo
12 Orion
13 On the moon
14 The sun
15 *Aurora australis*
16 Jupiter
17 The Dog Star
18 Pluto
19 c) 61
20 Uranus
21 Gemini
22 A solar eclipse
23 Because Pluto's orbit is elliptical, so it sometimes cuts inside the orbital path of Neptune
24 Coolest
25 Venus

Madonna
1 Ciccone
2 Drums
3 16 August
4 Sire
5 'Into the Groove'
6 *Desperately Seeking Susan*
7 Roseanna Arquette
8 Rocco
9 'Material Girl'
10 Lola
11 Alan Parker
12 A cliffside in Malibu
13 'Live to Tell'
14 Warren Beatty
15 Jean-Paul Gaultier
16 *Shanghai Surprise*
17 Maverick
18 Carlos Leon
19 *In Bed with Madonna*
20 Time Warner
21 Antonio Banderas
22 *True Blue*
23 Five
24 Ali G
25 John 'Jellybean' Benitez

The 1930s
1 Prohibition
2 Australia
3 The *Queen Mary*
4 The Crystal Palace
5 Amy Johnson
6 *Brave New World*
7 Poet Laureate
8 Darts
9 Thomas Edison
10 Donald Bradman

11 Hitler and Stalin
12 *Bluebird*
13 The Volkswagen
14 Peas
15 Clarence Birdseye
16 John Dillinger
17 Jesse Owens
18 Warfield
19 Empire State Building
20 *Gone With the Wind*
21 Sir Oswald Mosley
22 Orson Welles
23 The BBC
24 Dust storms
25 Brain tumor

Tennis
1 Australian Open, French Open, Wimbledon, US Open
2 Steffi Graf
3 Yevgeny Kafelnikov
4 Monica Seles
5 Czechoslovakia
6 The men's Olympic singles title
7 Jimmy Connors and John McEnroe
8 £750
9 Goran Ivanisevic
10 There wasn't one – the 1985 championship was the last one to be held in December, switching to January in 1987
11 Maureen Connolly
12 The US Open, 1999
13 Pete Sampras
14 Martina Hingis
15 40-15
16 Arthur Ashe
17 Sue Barker
18 Steffi Graf
19 Bjorn Borg
20 After the first seven games, then after every nine games
21 Virginia Wade
22 1995
23 Richard Krajicek, 1996
24 Ranking points
25 Margaret Court

TV Presenters
1 Ed Sullivan
2 Oprah Winfrey
3 Richard Dimbleby
4 Wolfman Jack
5 Walter Kronkite
6 Alan Freed
7 Jerry Springer
8 Alistair Cooke
9 Oprah Winfrey
10 TV news
11 Jean-Paul Gaultier
12 *The Tonight Show*

13 Murray the K
14 Alfred Hitchcock
15 Bill Maher
16 *Tales From the Crypt*
17 Ricki Lake
18 *The Larry Sanders Show*
19 *WRKP in Cincinnati*
20 Dan Rowan and Dick Martin
21 David Letterman
22 *The Outer Limits*
23 Clive James
24 Howard Stern
25 Chris Stevens, played by John Corbett

Mythology
1 Hermaphroditus
2 Atlas
3 China
4 Leviathan
5 Thoth
6 Valhalla
7 Woden or Wotan
8 The Minotaur
9 The Muses
10 Neptune
11 Python
12 Avalon
13 The Fianna or Fenians
14 Shiva
15 Ra
16 Morgan Le Fay
17 Orpheus
18 Avatars
19 Thor
20 Ancient Persia
21 Sir Galahad
22 Bodhisattva
23 The dragon
24 A cat
25 The Lady of the Lake

THE GREATEST TRIVIA QUIZ BOOK

QUIZ 6

1 What is the real name of the American rap star Eminem?

2 Who is the youngest man to win the Wimbledon singles title?

3 Who directed the 1946 Oscar-winning film *The Best Years of our Lives*?

4 Which cartoon character gets dumped outside his front door by the cat?

5 Who scored twice for France in the 1998 World Cup final?

6 *The Misfits* marked the last film appearance of two Hollywood legends. Clark Gable was one, who was the other?

7 By what name do we better know Doris von Kappelhoff?

8 Who assassinated Robert Kennedy?

9 Who takes it upon himself to teach Eliza Doolittle to speak properly?

10 Who plays the part of Richard Fish in *Ally McBeal*?

11 Who completed the tennis Grand Slam when he won the 1999 French title?

12 Who starred alongside Cary Grant in the film *His Girl Friday*?

13 Who was the fortieth president of the United States?

14 Which American golfer shares his surname with a style of music?

15 Who won the 1967 Eurovision Song Contest?

16 Who was the first black heavyweight boxing champion of the world?

17 What is the full name of the central character in Dickens's *Great Expectations*?

18 Which French actress has devoted most of her life to animal causes since her career ended?

19 Whose works include a painting inspired by the bombing of a town called Guernica in the Spanish Civil War?

20 Who was the star of the film *Mrs Miniver*?

21 Who is lead guitarist with The Kinks?

22 Under what name did the Police drummer have the solo hit 'Don't Care' in 1978?

23 Who directed the films *Ordinary People* and *A River Runs Through It*?

24 Which British boxer has won an Olympic gold medal for Canada?

25 Which character was played by Shelley Duvall opposite Robin Williams in a film of the adventures of a popular cartoon character?

1 Which Sergei Eisenstein film was released in January 1926?

2 In which of Rudolph Valentino's films did he play a bullfighter?

3 What was 'Fatty' Arbuckle's Christian name?

4 Which actress began her career in 1914 at the age of fifteen, went on to make several films with director Cecil B de Mille, and later played a fading movie star in the 1950 film *Sunset Boulevard*?

5 Which two stars of the silent screen married each other in 1920?

6 In which of his films does Charles Chaplin help a blind flower girl?

7 What was the title of the adventure serial starring Pearl White, which ran in conjunction with a weekly newspaper version?

8 On whom was the character of Susan Alexander based in Orson Welles's *Citizen Kane*?

9 Who directed *The Birth of a Nation*?

10 Whom did Mack Sennett sign at the end of 1913 for $150 per week?

11 Who was the star of the 1925 film *The Phantom of the Opera*?

12 By what nickname was actress Clara Bow known?

13 Who played Rudolph Valentino in Ken Russell's 1977 biopic of the silent star?

14 Which actress starred in such films as *The Birth of a Nation*, *Orphans of the Storm* and *The Wind*, and received a special Oscar in 1970?

15 What was the title of Robert Flaherty's 1922 documentary about Eskimo life?

16 Sharing its name with a famous British crime of the 1960s, which eleven-minute Western of 1903 is one of the first story films ever made?

17 Which two stars were brought together by producer Hal Roach in 1926?

18 Who directed, co-wrote and starred in the 1927 film *The General*?

19 What two words were used to promote Greta Garbo's 1930 film *Anna Christie*?

20 What was striking about comedy actor Ben Turpin's appearance?

21 In the 1923 film *Safety Last*, who is seen dangling from a clock face?

22 Jackie Coogan appeared in Chaplin's *The Kid* when he was six. Over forty years later he appeared on TV as a member of which family?

23 A huge hit in 1939 as a musical, which story by L Frank Baum was first filmed in 1910, and again in 1924?

24 Which group of uniformed actors made several slapstick comedies between 1912 and 1920?

25 What did four brothers called Harry, Sam, Albert and Jack start in 1923?

1 Which group of islands lies approximately 300 miles southwest of India?

2 Which is the largest of the Balearic Islands?

3 Which Pacific Island, famous for its giant sculptures of heads, is also known as Rapa Nui?

4 Which island lies off the west coast of mainland Canada, just over the border from the United States?

5 Of which large island in the Indian Ocean is Antananarivo the capital?

6 Between which two islands does the Denmark Strait flow?

7 Which island is larger, Trinidad or Tobago?

8 On which of the Hawaiian islands is the capital, Honolulu?

9 Which two countries make up the Caribbean island of Hispaniola?

10 In which ocean is Easter Island?

11 Of which country is Shikoku one of the four main islands?

12 In which lake would you find the Isle Royale National Park?

13 On which island is the volcanic Mount Etna?

14 Lying off England's northeast coast, by what name is Holy Island also known?

15 From which of the United States of America do the Aleutian Islands stretch into the Pacific Ocean?

16 Which island's features include Blue Mountain Peak, Portland Point and Montego Bay?

17 Under which country's administration are the islands of New Caledonia in the Coral Sea?

18 By what name do we know the islands that Spanish-speaking nations call the Islas Malvinas?

19 On which island are the New York boroughs of Brooklyn and Queens?

20 On which of the Channel Islands are cars not permitted?

21 Which Mediterranean island has Iraklion as its capital?

22 Which Indonesian island lies off the east coast of Java?

23 The scene of one of the Pacific battles during the Second World War, in which group of islands is Guadalcanal?

24 In which ocean is Christmas Island?

25 Where in Canada would you find Elk Island and Reindeer Island?

13

15

1 What is the connection between Gary Numan and Cliff Richard, apart from them both having UK number ones in 1979?

2 Which band connects Robert Palmer's 'Addicted to Love' and David Bowie's 'Let's Dance'?

3 Although poles apart musically, what connects Foreigner with The Clash?

4 What do Shirley Bassey, Sheena Easton and Duran Duran have in common?

5 What name connects the third symphony by Vaughan Williams to Beethoven's sixth?

6 What connects Frankie Goes to Hollywood, Jennifer Rush, and Huey Lewis and the News?

7 In terms of Grammy Awards, what connects Louis Armstrong, Mahalia Jackson and Charlie Parker?

8 Which musician links The Rolling Stones, The Jeff Beck Group and The Faces?

9 In addition to being UK number one singles, what connects Norman Greenbaum's 'Spirit in the Sky' to Fleetwood Mac's 'Albatross'?

10 What honour is shared by Irene Cara's hits 'Fame' and 'Flashdance...What a Feeling'?

11 With whom did Queen, Bing Crosby and Mick Jagger all record singles?

12 What connects the artists who recorded 'Say What You Want', 'Yummy Yummy Yummy', and 'The Ballad of Davy Crockett'?

13 In terms of UK charts, what connects Jim Reeves' 'Distant Drums', Jimi Hendrix's 'Voodoo Chile' and Elvis Presley's 'Way Down'?

14 What is the connection between Peter Gabriel's first four albums?

15 What is the connection between Stevie Wonder's 'Happy Birthday' and U2's 'Pride (In the Name of Love)'?

16 What do Van Halen, The Bachelors and Spandau Ballet have in common?

17 What is the connection between Richard, who sang 'Tutti Frutti' in 1957 and Eva, who sang 'The Loco-Motion' in 1962?

18 Which song was recorded by Bing Crosby and Grace Kelly, and also by Elton John and Kiki Dee?

19 What connects UK chart-toppers 'I Feel for You' by Chaka Khan and 'Nothing Compares 2 U' by Sinead O'Connor?

20 What do Abba have in common with Buddy Holly?

21 By what common nickname were jazz pianist Waller and rock & roll pianist Domino known?

22 Who recorded duets with Mary Wells, Kim Weston, Tammi Terrell and Diana Ross?

23 What connects Elvis Costello, Declan MacManus, Napoleon Dynamite and The Impostor?

24 The title of which Sam Cooke song, when inserted in the gap shown, completes a Louis Armstrong song title, and forms the first half of the title of a Jimmy Cliff hit:
What a .... Beautiful People?

25 What song links Badfinger, Narry Nilsson and Mariah Carey?

2

1 What material was invented by Belgian-born US chemist Leo Baekeland in 1905?

2 In 1905, Albert Einstein wrote that $E = mc^2$. What theory is commonly associated with this equation?

3 In the 1940s George Gamow developed a theory that a giant explosion, 10–20,000 million years ago, began the expansion of the universe. What is the name given to this theory?

4 A common sight in most high streets, what was invented in 1967 by Englishman John Shepherd-Barron?

5 Which metal was invented by British metallurgist Harold Brearley in 1912?

6 What nationality is Erno Rubik, inventor of the eighties craze the Rubik's Cube?

7 In which decade was the breathalyser invented?

8 First marketed in 1958 by the Kodak company as 'Eastman 910', by what name is their cyanoacrylate adhesive better known?

9 Which company introduced the first 'instamatic' camera in 1963?

10 Who discovered penicillin in 1928?

11 Which German aircraft company invented the ejector seat in 1942?

12 What did British engineer Christopher Cokerell invent in 1953?

13 In 1967 an American engineer invented a noise reduction system to which he gave his name. What is it called?

14 What fastening device, common on clothing, was invented by George Abraham in 1901?

15 What did Englishman Percy Shaw contribute to road safety in 1934?

16 What familiar roadside item, in which money is placed, was invented in 1935 by American journalist Carlton Magee?

17 In 1953 US surgeon Evarts Graham discovered the link between tobacco tar and what?

18 What nationality was inventor Léon Gaumont, who introduced a type of colour motion picture film in 1912?

19 Who invented the bouncing bomb in the Second World War?

20 In 1955 Dane Ole Christiansen invented a children's construction toy. Still in use today, and with theme parks of its own, what is it called?

21 Which drink machine was produced in 1946 by Italian inventor Achille Gaggia?

22 In which decade did German chemist Albert Hoffman discover Lyserg-Saure-Diathylamid, or lysergic acid diethylamide (LSD)?

23 Which hormone was discovered by Canadian and Scottish physiologists in 1912?

24 In 1901 which Italian inventor developed the first transatlantic telegraphy system?

25 Which water transport aid was invented by Norwegian-born engineer Ole Evinrude in 1906?

1 Which were the only three teams to beat Manchester United in the 1999/2000 season?

2 Which team plays at the Boleyn Ground?

3 Who has played in local derbies in Manchester and Liverpool and, most recently, Glasgow?

4 Which club did Nigerian international Daniel Amokachi join after the 1994 World Cup?

5 At the time of writing, which two players hold the record for most goals in a single Premiership season?

6 Which Czech Republic player joined Manchester United after Euro '96?

7 Who did Harry Redknapp replace as manager of West Ham United in 1994?

8 Who scored a wonderful individual goal for Derby County on his debut in their 3-2 win at Old Trafford in 1997?

9 Which team finished second in the Premiership in 1996 and 1997?

10 Which Blackburn Rovers strike partnership of the mid-nineties was known as SAS?

11 Which player joined Sheffield Wednesday from Inter Milan in 1996?

12 Which team did the Premier League and FA Cup double in 1997/98?

13 Which team rejoined the Premiership in 2000 after a four-year absence, during which time they spent one season in the Second Division?

14 Which award was won by Liverpool's Robbie Fowler in 1995 and 1996?

15 Which was the last season that the Premiership was contested over forty-two games?

16 Who was Arsenal's caretaker manager prior to the arrival of Arsène Wenger in November 1996?

17 Which Premiership team used to play at the Baseball Ground?

18 At which club's school of excellence did Ryan Giggs train until he was fourteen?

19 Who has been manager at Liverpool, Blackburn Rovers and Newcastle United?

20 Who was voted Carling Player of the Year for the 1999/2000 season?

21 Who were the last champions of the old First Division in 1992, prior to the formation of the Premier League?

22 About whom did George Best say, 'He can't head the ball, tackle or kick with his left foot and he doesn't score enough goals'?

23 Which three teams were relegated at the end of the 1999/2000 season?

24 Which club was deducted three points in 1996 for failing to fulfil a fixture at Blackburn?

25 Which Premiership club was formed in 1905 by a group of 14- and 15-year-olds living in streets by the Thames?

9

1 Which American series of the 1960s starred Richard Chamberlain as the eponymous hero?

2 What was the name of the hospital given the nickname St Elsewhere in the show of the same name?

3 What is the title of the New Zealand soap set in and around a hospital?

4 What branch of medicine did ER's Dr Douglas Ross, aka George Clooney, specialise in?

5 In which American series does actress Christine Lahti don the white coat?

6 Which famous big-screen actor played Dr Philip Chandler in St Elsewhere?

7 What do the initials M*A*S*H stand for?

8 Which hospital show featured a pathologist who had a penchant for making love in the morgue?

9 How did Lucy Knight make her exit from ER?

10 Which two members of the Ally McBeal team, one in front of camera, one behind, once worked on Chicago Hope?

11 Blair General Hospital was the setting for which hospital show?

12 In the final show of which series was the hospital in which it was set revealed to be a model inside a toy snowstorm?

13 Before gaining worldwide fame in ER, George Clooney appeared in an eighties hospital comedy with Elliott Gould. What was it called?

14 Between 1961 and 1966 Vince Edwards played the title role in which American series?

15 Which characters in *M*A*S*H* were engaged in an affair?

16 Who directed the 1970 movie *M*A*S*H* that inspired the TV series?

17 Which *ER* actress appeared as Laura Kelly in *NYPD Blue*?

18 What is the name of the character played by Alex Kingston in *ER*?

19 Which hospital show starred Mandy Pantinkin?

20 In which US city was *St Elsewhere* set?

21 Sheryl Lee plays Sarah Church in *L.A. Doctors*. What was her breakthrough TV Role?

22 Which Canadian-born stand-up comedian played Dr Wayne Fiscus in *St Elsewhere*?

23 Which Australian hospital show was set in the outback town of Cooper's Crossing?

24 Which 1960s hospital series opened with the line 'Man, woman, birth, death, infinity'?

25 The final episode of which show was titled 'Goodbye, Farewell and Amen'?

1 What do the initials MG stand for?

2 Who first used electric ignition by battery and coil in 1886?

3 Which Lotus car came on the market in 1963 and featured in *The Avengers*?

4 Predating the Model T Ford, which was the world's first car to be made in large quantities, 19,000 being sold between 1902 and 1906?

5 What is represented by the blue and white quartered circle of the BMW logo?

6 The E-type Jaguar was introduced in fixed-head coupé form at the 1961 Geneva Motor Show. To the nearest hundred pounds, what was its original selling price?

7 What type of car did Michael Caine drive in the film *Get Carter*?

8 What was the significance of the number 40 in relation to the Ford GT40?

9 Which British sports car company was founded in 1962 by Jem Marsh and Frank Costin, whose names inspired the more continental-sounding company name?

10 What make of car did Don McLean drive to the levee in 'American Pie'?

11 Which car was first patented in 1909?

12 What do the initials DB stand for in conjunction with Aston Martin?

13 Which British car company's first car was the two-seater Oxford in 1913?

20

14 Which British car was driven by Paddy Hopkirk to win the 1964 Monte Carlo rally, and also featured in the film *The Italian Job*?

15 Why was the Jaguar XJ220 so named?

16 Which now-standard fittings were first featured on a car in 1916?

17 Which Italian company's emblem features a raging bull?

18 In which country is the Daewoo company based?

19 Which model Ferrari has a name which means 'redhead'?

20 Why did Henry Ford say that people could have a Model T in any colour so long as it was black?

21 Which company began manufacturing the Jeep in 1943?

22 What do the initials SLK mean in relation to the Mercedes car of that name?

23 Which American car of the 1940s had a third central headlight that swivelled with the front wheels?

24 In which year did the Volkswagen Beetle make its first appearance?

25 The world's first motorway opened in 1924. In which country?

ANSWERS TO QUIZ 6

Double Initials
1 Marshall Mathers
2 Boris Becker
3 William Wyler
4 Fred Flintstone
5 Zinedine Zidane
6 Marilyn Monroe
7 Doris Day
8 Sirhan Sirhan
9 Henry Higgins
10 Greg Germann
11 Andre Agassi
12 Rosalind Russell
13 Ronald Reagan
14 Fred Funk
15 Sandie Shaw
16 Jack Johnson
17 Philip Pirrip
18 Brigitte Bardot
19 Pablo Picasso
20 Greer Garson
21 Dave Davies
22 Klark Kent
23 Robert Redford
24 Lennox Lewis
25 Olive Oyl

The Silent Era
1 *Battleship Potemkin*
2 *Blood and Sand*
3 Roscoe
4 Gloria Swanson
5 Douglas Fairbanks and Mary Pickford
6 *City Lights*
7 *The Perils of Pauline*
8 Marion Davies
9 D W Griffith
10 Charles Chaplin
11 Lon Chaney
12 The 'It' Girl
13 Rudolf Nureyev
14 Lillian Gish
15 *Nanook of the North*
16 *The Great Train Robbery*
17 Stan Laurel and Oliver Hardy
18 Buster Keaton
19 Garbo talks
20 He was cross-eyed
21 Harold Lloyd
22 The Addams family – Uncle Fester
23 *The Wizard of Oz*
24 The Keystone Kops
25 Warner Brothers Pictures Inc

Islands
1 The Maldives
2 Majorca
3 Easter Island
4 Vancouver Island
5 Madagascar
6 Greenland and Iceland
7 Trinidad
8 Oahu
9 Haiti and the Dominican Republic
10 Pacific
11 Japan
12 Lake Superior
13 Sicily
14 Lindisfarne
15 Alaska
16 Jamaica
17 France
18 The Falkland Islands
19 Long Island
20 Sark
21 Crete
22 Bali
23 The Solomon Islands
24 Indian
25 Lake Winnipeg

Connections
1 Both were born with the surname Webb
2 Chic: Bernard Edwards and Nile Rodgers produced respectively
3 Both had members called Mick Jones
4 They all recorded James Bond themes
5 They are both known as 'Pastoral' symphonies
6 They all released singles called 'The Power of Love'
7 They all received the Lifetime Achievement Award posthumously
8 Ron Wood
9 Fleetwood Mac guitarist Peter Green was born Peter Greenbaum
10 They are both Oscar-winning songs
11 David Bowie
12 American states – Texas, Ohio Express and Tennessee, Ernie Ford
13 They were all posthumous number ones
14 They were all called *Peter Gabriel*
15 They are both about Martin Luther King, Jr
16 They all have two brothers in the group
17 They were both known as 'Little'
18 'True Love'
19 They were both written by Prince
20 They have both inspired stage musicals
21 Fats
22 Marvin Gaye
23 They are the same person
24 'Wonderful World'
25 'Without You'

Inventions & Discoveries
1 Bakelite
2 The theory of relativity
3 The Big Bang theory
4 The cash dispenser
5 Stainless steel
6 Hungarian
7 1930s
8 Superglue
9 Kodak
10 Alexander Fleming
11 Heinkel
12 The hovercraft
13 Dolby
14 The press-stud
15 He invented cats'-eyes
16 The parking meter
17 Cancer
18 French
19 Barnes Wallis
20 Lego
21 Espresso coffee machine
22 1940s
23 Insulin
24 Guglielmo Marconi
25 The outboard motor

The Premiership
1 Chelsea, Newcastle United and Tottenham Hotspur
2 West Ham United (Boleyn Ground, Green Street, Upton Park)
3 Andrei Kanchelskis
4 Everton
5 Andy Cole and Alan Shearer, both with 34
6 Karel Poborsky
7 Billy Bonds
8 Paulo Wanchope
9 Newcastle United
10 Alan Shearer and Chris Sutton
11 Benito Carbone
12 Arsenal
13 Manchester City
14 PFA Young Player of the Year
15 1994/95
16 Stewart Houston
17 Derby County
18 Manchester City
19 Kenny Dalglish
20 Kevin Phillips
21 Leeds United
22 David Beckham
23 Wimbledon, Sheffield Wednesday and Watford
24 Middlesbrough
25 Charlton Athletic

Hospital Dramas
1 *Dr Kildare*
2 St Eligius
3 *Shortland Street*
4 Paediatrics
5 *Chicago Hope*
6 Denzel Washington
7 Mobile Army Surgical Hospital
8 *St Elsewhere*
9 She was stabbed to death
10 Writer/producer David E Kelley and actor Peter MacNicol
11 *Dr Kildare*
12 *St Elsewhere*
13 Coincidentally, it was called *E/R*
14 *Ben Casey*
15 Margaret 'Hot Lips' Hoolihan and Frank Burns
16 Robert Altman
17 Sherry Stringfield
18 Dr Elizabeth Corday
19 *Chicago Hope*
20 Boston
21 Laura Palmer in *Twin Peaks*
22 Howie Mandel
23 *The Flying Doctors*
24 *Ben Casey*
25 *M*A*S*H*

Cars
1 Morris Garages
2 Karl Benz
3 The Elan
4 The Curved Dash Oldsmobile
5 A spinning propeller
6 £1,550
7 Jaguar Mk II 3.4
8 It stood 40 inches tall
9 Marcos
10 Chevy
11 Model-T Ford
12 David Brown (one-time owner of the company)
13 Morris
14 Mini Cooper
15 Its top speed was 220 mph
16 Automatic windscreen wipers
17 Lamborghini
18 Korea
19 Testarossa
20 Japan black enamel was the only colour that would dry quickly enough to keep up with the assembly line
21 Willys
22 *Sportlich, Licht, Kompact* (Sporty, Light, Compact)
23 Tucker Torpedo
24 1945
25 Italy

THE GREATEST TRIVIA QUIZ BOOK

QUIZ 7

1 Whose baby was Bruno Hauptmann accused of kidnapping and killing in 1932?

2 Hanged at Wandsworth prison in 1949 for killing six people, by what title was John George Haigh known?

3 Who was electrocuted in January 1989 after murdering between nineteen and forty people between 1974 and 1977?

4 Which unidentified murderer was known as the 'Whitechapel Murderer', as well as by his more common nickname?

5 Subject of a film starring Richard Attenborough, who lived at 10 Rillington Place, London?

6 Who became Surveyor of the Queen's Pictures in 1972, despite confessing to being a Soviet spy twelve years earlier?

7 John Dillinger was shot by FBI agents outside a cinema in which city?

8 Why were the death sentences of the Manson family commuted to life imprisonment in 1972?

9 Who was responsible for the deaths of seventeen young men in Wisconsin and Ohio and was murdered by a fellow prisoner?

10 Which pair of 19th-century killers sold their victims' bodies to the medical profession?

11 Who claimed thirteen victims in the north of England between 1975 and 1980?

12 According to legend, who 'took an axe and gave her mother forty whacks'?

13 Who hanged himself in his prison cell on New Year's Day 1995, before being tried for the crimes he committed?

14 Although involved in various murders, including the 'St Valentine's Day Massacre', for what was Al Capone eventually imprisoned?

15 Which two sons of millionaires, themselves only teenagers, killed a fourteen-year-old boy in 1924 for kicks?

16 Who, in 1986, admitted to the murders of Pauline Reade and Keith Bennett more than two decades before?

17 By what nickname was mobster Benjamin Siegel better known?

18 Who was the last woman to be hanged in Britain, on 13 July 1955?

19 The *Montrose* was one of the first ships equipped with Marconi's radio telegraph. Which passenger did this invention help bring to justice for his wife's murder in 1910?

20 On 23 May 1934, a Miss Parker and a Mr Barrow were killed in a hail of police gunfire. What were the first names of these two, who had killed 13 people?

21 By which name was thirties New York gangster Arthur Flegenheimer better known?

22 In which year were Ronald and Reginald Kray sentenced to life imprisonment for the murders of George Cornell and Jack 'The Hat' McVitie?

23 Which gang boss, who took over Al Capone's old Chicago territory, was shot dead by intruders at his home in 1975?

24 By what name was Albert De Salvo better known?

25 By what name was Salvatore Luciana better known?

1 Which actress won an Oscar for her role as a bimbo in *Mighty Aphrodite*?

2 In which film does an actor step out of the cinema screen to confront a woman sitting in the stalls?

3 In which 1975 film did Woody Allen star as a restaurant cashier and small-time bookie who is hired to lend his name to TV scripts written by blacklisted writers?

4 In which film do a pair of burglars answer the telephone and become random contestants in a phone-in quiz show?

5 What was Allen's first film as director?

6 Which character did Allen play in *Casino Royale*?

7 Which of Allen's films is about a comedy director in mid-life and career crisis?

8 In which film is Allen's character resuscitated in the 22nd century?

9 Who played Hannah in *Hannah and her Sisters*?

10 Which composer's music was used extensively in *Manhattan*?

11 Which film is about a playwright having his play backed by a mobster, whose girlfriend has to be given a starring role?

12 Which film has Allen as a Russian countryman at the time of the Napoleonic wars?

13 In which film did Allen and Diane Keaton first star together?

14 Who played Allen's smug TV producer brother-in-law in *Crimes and Misdemeanors*?

15 Which two directors, along with Woody Allen, were responsible for the 1989 movie *New York Stories*?

16 In 1979 Allen directed and co-narrated a short film entitled *My Favorite Comedian*. Who was the film's subject?

17 In which film does Allen star as a small-time variety agent?

18 For which film did Allen receive Oscars for direction and original screenplay?

19 In which film does Allen's character become involved in politics, eventually becoming president of San Marcos?

20 Which film's central character is described as a 'human chameleon'?

21 In which film did Allen make his acting debut?

22 Which instrument does Allen play in his New Orleans-style jazz band?

23 Which film's release coincided, ironically, with Allen's break-up with Mia Farrow?

24 Who was Allen's co-star in *Scenes from a Mall*?

25 The original script ideas for *Annie Hall* became the basis of which later movie, again co-starring Diane Keaton?

2

1 Butterflies and moths are in the insect group Lepidoptera. Which group contains ants, bees and wasps?

2 Which insect is popular with gardeners because it feeds on aphids?

3 What type of insects are hawkers, clubtails, biddies, emeralds, darts and skimmers?

4 What are the three divisions of an insect's body?

5 Female honeybees that receive royal jelly throughout their larval stage develop into what?

6 Which aptly-named spider devours its partner after mating?

7 Why is the mole cricket so called?

8 What name is given to the study of insects?

9 From which material do wasps build their nests?

10 Which insect transmits African sleeping sickness?

11 What is an ovipositor?

12 Which stage of an insect's life cycle comes between egg and pupa?

13 Does the male or female horsefly feed on blood?

14 What is the common name for the crane fly?

15 What are insects' chewing jaws called?

16 Do butterflies usually rest with their wings together or open?

17 How long can a stag beetle spend as a larva?

18 Found on plants, what is the protective bubbly section of the nymphs of the spittle bug commonly called?

19 There are four classes of myriapods, two of which are pauropoda and symphyla. What are the two better known classes called?

20 Which insect can infect humans with malaria?

21 What type of insect is a weevil?

22 Which insect has a pair of prominent pincers at the tip of its abdomen?

23 Which is the largest species of beetle?

24 Which shiny insect feeds on such materials as wallpaper paste and bookbindings?

25 What is an exoskeleton?

10

1 In which US city was Motown records founded?

2 Which group was originally called The Primettes?

3 Who founded the Motown label?

4 Which vocal group, formed in 1954 as The Four Aims, gave the Motown label its first UK number one single in 1966?

5 Which white Motown singer/songwriter had hits with 'Indiana Wants Me' and 'There's a Ghost in My House'?

6 Which singer began his career in The Moonglows, with Motown boss Berry Gordy's brother-in-law Harvey Fuqua?

7 Which Motown singer/songwriter was once described by Bob Dylan as America's greatest living poet?

8 Which instrument did Stevie Wonder play on his breakthrough single 'Fingertips, pt 2'?

9 Which artist, along with his All Stars, had a hit with '(I'm a) Road Runner'?

10 What was Diana Ross's last hit with The Supremes?

11 Who had a hit in 1962 with 'Please Mr Postman'?

12 To which city did Motown move its headquarters in 1971?

13 What was the name on the front of the first Motown office and studio building in Detroit?

14 Which two Motown artists recorded duets with Paul McCartney?

15 Which of Marvin Gaye's singing partners died of a brain tumor in 1970?

16 What was Stevie Wonder's first album on gaining artistic control of his own output in 1972?

17 How old was Smokey Robinson when the Miracles released their first hit, 'Got a Job'?

18 Which two groups combined on the 1969 hit 'I'm Gonna Make You Love Me'?

19 Which group was the label's biggest selling act of the 1990s?

20 Why did The Jackson Five change their name to The Jacksons when they left Motown?

21 Which instruments were played by Motown session men James Jamerson and Benny Benjamin respectively?

22 Who sang lead on the hits 'Heat Wave', 'Jimmy Mack' and 'Nowhere to Run'?

23 With which group do you associate David Ruffin and Eddie Kendricks?

24 An untypical Motown record, which single gave singer Charlene a UK number one in 1982?

25 When The Supremes hit the number one spot in the UK in 1965 with 'Baby Love' it was not released on Motown, but on which other label?

17

1 Who wrote *The Naked and the Dead*?

2 Which conflict provided the setting for Ernest Hemingway's *For Whom the Bell Tolls*?

3 Which author inspired the names of bands Steely Dan and Soft Machine?

4 What was the title of beat writer Jack Kerouac's story of a journey across America by car?

5 Who wrote *The Witches of Eastwick*?

6 Who is the most famous creation of Edgar Rice Burroughs?

7 Which American writer was married to poet Ted Hughes?

8 Which Tom Wolfe story was made into a film by Brian de Palma, starring Tom Hanks and Bruce Willis?

9 Whose books include *The World According to Garp*, *The Hotel New Hampshire* and *The Cider House Rules*?

10 Which author took a bus full of 'Merry Pranksters' on a three-year bus trip around America, filming the country and its people?

11 Who created the character Jack Ryan, hero of such stories as *Patriot Games*, *Clear and Present Danger* and *The Hunt for Red October*?

12 What was Erica Jong's first novel, published in 1973?

13 Whose last book was *The Last Tycoon*?

14 Which crime writer's work includes *The Big Sleep*, *The Lady in The Lake* and *The Long Goodbye*?

15 Who has written under the name Richard Bachman?

16 Whose book *Rosinante to the Road Again* is set in Spain after the first World War?

17 Which poet's work includes *Just Give Me a Cool Drink of Water 'fore I Die*?

18 Who wrote *The Maltese Falcon*?

19 Whose book *The Right Stuff* deals with the early years of the American space programme?

20 Whose thrillers include *The Ostermen Weekend*, *The Bourne Identity* and *The Prometheus Deception*?

21 Who wrote the Pulitzer Prize-winning novel *To Kill a Mockingbird*?

22 Recently made into a film, who wrote the book *American Psycho*?

23 For which particular genre is Zane Grey best known?

24 Which writer moved to England in 1977 and whose work includes *Mother Tongue*, *The Lost Continent* and *Made in America*?

25 Which short story writer, humorist and illustrator wrote, among others, *My World – and Welcome to It*?

1 The winner of the 2000 Grand National shares his name with the title of which 1973 movie starring Steve McQueen and Dustin Hoffman?

2 Which horse 'won' the void Grand National of 1993?

3 On which English racecourse is the Cesarewitch run?

4 Who was flat racing's champion jockey from 1988–91, riding 728 winners?

5 Which National Hunt legend was known as 'Dessie'?

6 Ascot, Flemington and Randwick are racecourses in which country?

7 What was the name of comedian Freddie Starr's horse that won the 1994 Grand National?

8 Which National Hunt racecourse is in Staffordshire?

9 Members of which family owned all the Epsom Oaks winners from 1987 to 1991?

10 'The Choirboy' won the 1981 Epsom Derby riding Shergar. Who is 'The Choirboy'?

11 Which race is run on a course that extends over two English counties?

12 The Knavesmire is the racecourse of which English city?

13 The Belmont Stakes, the Kentucky Derby and which other race make up the US Triple Crown?

14 Who is 'The Long Fellow'?

15 In which year did Red Rum complete his hat trick of Grand National victories?

16 Which is the oldest of the English Classics, dating from the same year the American Revolution began?

17 Whose racing colours consist of a purple jacket with red sleeves, both with gold braid trim, and a black cap with gold tassel?

18 Phoenix Park racecourse is in which country?

19 In which country was trainer Sir Michael Stoute born?

20 Which horse won the Cheltenham Gold Cup in 1964, 1965 and 1966?

21 Pimlico and Aqueduct are racecourses in which country?

22 Which trainer, now retired, is known as 'The Duke'?

23 In which year did Lester Piggott ride his last English Classic winner?

24 The Roodeye is which English city's racecourse?

25 In racing slang how much is a 'pony' worth?

15

1 Which two stars of a current US sitcom have formed their own production company called Bristol Cities?

2 Which dame of British theatre is James Bond's latest boss and has recently completed another series on TV playing opposite Geoffrey Palmer?

3 Who plays Alicia Witt and Deedee Pfeiffer's screen mother in her own US sitcom?

4 Who played the only female cab driver in *Taxi*?

5 Who replaced Farrah Fawcett-Majors in *Charlie's Angels*?

6 Who played Ross's British wife in *Friends*?

7 Who played Samantha, the nose-twitching witch, in *Bewitched*?

8 Who connects seventies sitcom *Rhoda* with *The Simpsons*?

9 Who formed a production company called Desilu with her husband Desi Arnaz?

10 Who did Kirstie Alley replace in *Cheers*?

11 Which star of *Absolutely Fabulous* once played a crime-fighter alongside Patrick Macnee and Gareth Hunt?

12 Which British actress, famous for her role as Elizabeth I in a 1970s TV series, became a Labour MP in 1992?

13 Who replaced Barbara Bel Geddes in the role of Miss Ellie Ewing for a short time on *Dallas*?

14 Who played Mrs Bennett in the BBC's 1995 production of *Pride and Prejudice*?

15 Which ex-Benny Hill girl is part of a multi-Emmy-winning comedy show?

16 Which actress appears in both *Ally McBeal* and *ER*?

17 Now a star in Hollywood, who came to TV screens in a homely 1991 series based on novels by H E Bates?

18 Who appeared dishevelled as a prisoner of war in *Tenko* and as glamorous as it gets in *Dynasty*?

19 Which actress/comedienne has starred with two different surnames and with no surname at all?

20 Which family's mother was played by Miss Michael Learned?

21 How were veteran actresses Helen Hayes and Mildred Natwick known in a lighthearted detective series in the 1970s?

22 Which former model and child star is the central character in *Suddenly Susan*?

23 Sarah Michelle Geller plays Buffy the Vampire Slayer in the TV series of the same name, but who played the part in the 1992 Buffy film?

24 Which actress co-starred in *The Dick Van Dyke Show* and went on to have her own series, which itself spawned a couple of spin-offs?

25 Which established star of a US sitcom was originally due to play the part of Roz Doyle in *Frasier*?

1 Which company started as the Pacific Aero Products Company in 1916, was given its present name in 1917, and is today the largest aviation company in the world?

2 What do the initials IATA stand for?

3 Which term is used for electronic instruments for use in aviation?

4 Which acronym is used for the long-range radar surveillance and control centre for air defence developed originally in the USA?

5 Which engine powered both the Spitfire and Hurricane fighters of World War II?

6 Who was the first woman to fly solo across the Atlantic Ocean?

7 The worst midair collision in history was in 1997 between a Saudi Boeing 747 and a Kazak airliner that claimed the lives of all 349 on board. Near which city did it occur?

8 Which aviation company produces the DC series of aircraft?

9 What is Charles E 'Chuck' Yeager's claim to fame in aviation?

10 In which country did Charles Lindbergh land after the first solo transatlantic flight in 1927?

11 What was the name of the Java-born Dutch aircraft manufacturer who, during World War I, produced more than 40 types of airplanes for the German High Command?

12 Which aircraft manufacturer produced the Spitfire?

13 What was the family name of the French brothers who were pioneer developers of the hot-air balloon and who conducted the first untethered flights?

14 Who was chief of aeronautical research and development at the British Aircraft Corporation 1945 to 1971, having previously designed the Wellington bomber of World War II?

15 Which company produced the world's first commercial jet airliner?

16 Who made the world's first over-the-ocean flight in a heavier-than-air craft?

17 What name was given to the Boeing B-52 heavy bomber that first flew in 1952?

18 What is the name of the Russian-born US pioneer in aircraft design who is best known for his successful development of the helicopter?

19 Who was dubbed 'Queen of the Air' by the British press in the 1930s after her solo flight from England to Australia?

20 Sydney's main airport is named after which great Australian aviator?

22 How was the Mitsubishi A6M fighter aircraft better known?

23 The Lockheed F-117 Nighthawk was the first of which type of aircraft?

24 Which famous series of aircraft was designed by Artem Mikoyan and Mikhail Gurevich?

25 Which famous aircraft of World War II had a frame of wood and a skin of plywood, and was glued and screwed together in England, Canada, and Australia?

ANSWERS TO QUIZ 7

Criminals
1 Aviator Charles Lindbergh
2 The Acid Bath Murderer
3 Ted Bundy
4 Jack the Ripper
5 John Christie
6 Anthony Blunt
7 Chicago
8 California abolished the death penalty
9 Jeffrey Dahmer
10 Burke and Hare
11 Peter Sutcliffe, the Yorkshire Ripper
12 Lizzie Borden
13 Fred West
14 Tax evasion
15 Leopold and Loeb
16 Myra Hindley
17 Bugsy
18 Ruth Ellis
19 Dr Crippen
20 Bonnie and Clyde
21 Dutch Schultz
22 1969
23 Sam Giancana
24 The Boston Strangler
25 'Lucky' Luciano

Woody Allen
1 Mira Sorvino
2 *The Purple Rose of Cairo*
3 *The Front*
4 *Radio Days*
5 *Take the Money and Run*
6 Jimmy Bond
7 *Stardust Memories*
8 *Sleeper*
9 Mia Farrow
10 George Gershwin
11 *Bullets Over Broadway*
12 *Love and Death*
13 *Play It Again, Sam*
14 Alan Alda
15 Martin Scorsese and Francis Coppola
16 Bob Hope
17 *Broadway Danny Rose*
18 *Annie Hall*
19 *Bananas*
20 *Zelig*
21 *What's New, Pussycat?*
22 Clarinet
23 *Husbands and Wives*
24 Bette Midler
25 *Manhattan Murder Mystery*

Insects & Spiders
1 Hymenoptera
2 The ladybird
3 Dragonflies
4 Head, thorax and abdomen
5 Queens
6 The Black Widow

7 It spends most of its time underground
8 Entomology
9 Wood fibre
10 The tsetse fly
11 It is an appendage through which a female insect lays her eggs
12 Larva
13 The female
14 Daddy-longlegs
15 Mandibles
16 Together
17 Up to three years
18 Cuckoo spit
19 Centipedes and millipedes
20 The mosquito
21 A beetle
22 The earwig
23 The Goliath beetle
24 The silverfish
25 An insect's external skeleton

Tamla Motown
1 Detroit
2 The Supremes
3 Berry Gordy, Jr
4 The Four Tops
5 R Dean Taylor
6 Marvin Gaye
7 Smokey Robinson
8 Harmonica
9 Junior Walker
10 'Someday We'll Be Together'
11 The Marvelettes
12 Los Angeles
13 Hitsville USA
14 Stevie Wonder and Michael Jackson
15 Tammi Terrell
16 *Music of My Mind*
17 It was released on his eighteenth birthday
18 Diana Ross and The Supremes and The Temptations
19 Boyz II Men
20 Motown owned the name 'Jackson Five'
21 Bass and drums
22 Martha Reeves
23 The Temptations
24 'I've Never Been to Me'
25 Stateside

American Writers
1 Norman Mailer
2 Spanish Civil War
3 William Burroughs
4 *On the Road*
5 John Updike
6 Tarzan

7 Sylvia Plath
8 *The Bonfire of the Vanities*
9 John Irving
10 Ken Kesey
11 Tom Clancy
12 *Fear of Flying*
13 F Scott Fitzgerald
14 Raymond Chandler
15 Stephen King
16 John Dos Passos
17 Maya Angelou
18 Dashiell Hammett
19 Tom Wolfe
20 Robert Ludlum
21 Harper Lee
22 Brett Easton Ellis
23 The Western
24 Bill Bryson
25 James Thurber

Horse Racing
1 Papillon
2 Esha Ness
3 Newmarket
4 Pat Eddery
5 Desert Orchid
6 Australia
7 Miinnehoma
8 Uttoxeter
9 Maktoum
10 Walter Swinburn
11 The Cesarewitch (starts in Cambridgeshire, finishes in Suffolk)
12 York
13 Preakness Stakes
14 Lester Piggott
15 1977
16 St Leger
17 HM Queen Elizabeth II
18 Ireland
19 Barbados
20 Arkle
21 USA
22 David Nicholson
23 1992 (St Leger on Rodrigo di Triano)
24 Chester
25 £25

Female Stars
1 Jane Leeves and Peri Gilpin (Daphne and Roz in *Frasier*)
2 Judi Dench
3 Cybill Shepherd
4 Marilu Henner
5 Cheryl Ladd
6 Helen Baxendale
7 Elizabeth Montgomery
8 Julie Kavner (she played Rhoda's sister and she is the voice of Marge Simpson)
9 Lucille Ball
10 Shelley Long (but not as the same character)

11 Joanna Lumley
12 Glenda Jackson
13 Donna Reed
14 Alison Steadman
15 Jane Leeves
16 Lisa Nicole Carson
17 Catherine Zeta Jones
18 Stephanie Beacham
19 Roseanne
20 The Waltons
21 The Snoop Sisters
22 Brooke Shields
23 Kristy Swanson
24 Mary Tyler Moore
25 Lisa Kudrow (Phoebe in *Friends*)

Aviation
1 Boeing
2 International Air Transport Association
3 Avionics
4 AWACS
5 Rolls-Royce Merlin
6 Beryl Markham
7 New Delhi
8 McDonnell-Douglas
9 First man to fly faster than the speed of sound
10 France
11 Anthony Fokker
12 Supermarine
13 Montgolfier
14 Barnes Wallis
15 De Havilland (the Comet)
16 Louis Bleriot
17 Stratofortress
18 Igor Sikorsky
19 Amy Johnson
20 Sir Charles Kingsford-Smith
22 Zero
23 Stealth
24 MiG
25 De Havilland Mosquito

THE GREATEST TRIVIA QUIZ BOOK

QUIZ 8

1 Which Rugby Union player created a world record by playing in 53 consecutive matches for Wales between 1967 and 1978?

2 Who left to his wife his 'second-best bed'?

3 Who weighed nearly 53 stone (742 lb, 337 kg) at his death in 1809?

4 Which very famous lady was christened with the name of the city in which she was born?

5 Which footballer made 106 appearances for England, scoring 49 international goals?

6 What are the Christian names of Torvill and Dean?

7 Which bestselling author wrote *The Cruel Sea*?

8 In terms of their names what do Paul McCartney and Harold Wilson have in common?

9 Which character actor made his name in the 1978 TV serial *Pennies from Heaven*?

10 Who was born in 1758 at Burnham Thorpe, Norfolk and died at the age of 47?

11 Which Prime Minister won the Nobel Prize for literature?

12 In which year did Sharron Davies first compete in an Olympic Games?

13 What was the surname of the artist whose forenames were Joseph Mallord William?

14 How is Emma Bunton better known?

15 Who first became well known writing radio scripts with Frank Muir?

16 Which Rugby player was known as 'The King'?

17 Which jockey rode Aldaniti to victory in the 1981 Grand National, having spent the previous two years winning a battle with cancer?

18 Which famous soldier was drowned when HMS *Hampshire* sank after striking a mine in 1916?

19 Which British actor had to change his name because there was already a very famous James Stewart?

20 Which actor was married to actresses Vivien Leigh and Joan Plowright (at different times, of course!)?

21 Who won the women's singles championship at Wimbledon in 1961?

22 Who was the original question master on *University Challenge*?

23 Which impresario, who shares a name with an item of clothing, is famous for staging hit musicals such as *Cats*, *Miss Saigon* and *Les Misérables*?

24 What was the name of the twenty-four-year-old RAF bomber pilot who led the Dam Busters raid?

25 Who is the only Briton to have won the Formula One world motor racing championship three times?

6

1 Who directed and starred in the 1942 film *The Goose Steps Out*?

2 Who played a character called Flash Harry in the St Trinian's films?

3 Which song was playing when the men started to dance in the dole queue in *The Full Monty*?

4 Which actor got locked outside in his underpants in *Notting Hill*?

5 Which political group was led by John Cleese in Monty Python's *Life of Brian*?

6 In which film did Alec Guinness, Cecil Parker, Herbert Lom, Peter Sellers and Danny Green play criminals posing as a group of musicians?

7 Which Oscar Wilde comedy was made into a film in 1952, starring Michael Redgrave and Edith Evans?

8 Who played Louis Mazzini, the man who murders his way through the d'Ascoyne family, in *Kind Hearts and Coronets*?

9 Which film saw Tony Hancock quit his job in the city to become an artist in Paris?

10 Who played the lead role in the film *Drop Dead Fred*?

11 How was the stolen gold bullion to be exported in *The Lavender Hill Mob*?

12 Which diminutive British comedian made a rare screen appearance in *Fierce Creatures*?

13 Which 1960 black comedy gave its title to a radio and TV series featuring a village full of bizarre characters?

14 In which Mike Leigh bittersweet comedy did Brenda Blethyn receive an Oscar nomination in 1996?

15 Who played inventor Sidney Stratton in *The Man in The White Suit*?

16 Which actor played the character who dies in *Four Weddings and a Funeral*?

17 Who played Uncle Monty in *Withnail and I*?

18 In the 1951 film *Laughter in Paradise* four people have to fulfil tasks in order to receive an inheritance. Who plays the man who must spend 28 days in jail?

19 Which comedy duo starred in the 1967 film *Bedazzled*, and also wrote the screenplay?

20 Who played King Arthur in *Monty Python and the Holy Grail*?

21 Who was the George in the 1940s films *South American George*, *Bell-Bottom George* and *George in Civvy Street*?

22 In which film do Ian Carmichael and Terry-Thomas meet on the tennis court?

23 Which brothers produced and directed such films as *Private's Progress*, *Carlton Browne of the FO*, and *I'm All Right, Jack*?

24 Which 1994 black comedy involves three young people disposing of a dead body and keeping the man's money?

25 Who was the leading actor in the films *Doctor in the House*, *Doctor at Sea* and *Doctor at Large*?

135

13

1 Which National Park includes the Black Mountains and Usk Valley?

2 What is the most famous landmark on the second-largest of the Orkney Islands?

3 Which Irish river, the site of a famous battle, rises in the Bog of Allen, County Kildare and enters the Irish Sea just south of Drogheda?

4 Which river forms most of the boundary between the English counties of Essex and Suffolk?

5 Lying at the southern edge of the Highlands, which is the largest lake in Scotland?

6 What are McGillycuddy's Reeks?

7 Featured in the TV series *The Prisoner*, what is the name of the Italianate Welsh village designed by architect Clough Williams-Ellis?

8 Where is Alum Bay, which is famous for its many-coloured sandstone cliffs?

9 Which part of south Staffordshire was originally a royal preserve and hunting forest and includes large areas of forestry?

10 Which range of hills forms a 30-mile stretch of the border between England and Scotland?

11 Which island in the English Channel was known as 'Sarnia' to the Romans?

12 Which island in the Irish Sea is roughly equidistant from the coasts of England, Ireland and Scotland?

13 In which national park would you find the peaks Skiddaw, Helvellyn and Great Gable?

14 What is the northernmost point of the British mainland?

15 Ynys Mon is the largest island in England and Wales. By what name is it known in English?

16 On which river is the High Force waterfall?

17 Wookey Hole is part of which range of hills?

18 Which feature of the east of England was caused by the flooding of medieval peat diggings?

19 Ripon is the tourist centre for which National Park?

20 Until about 5000 BC it was a river valley, now the French call it the Pas de Calais. How is it known in English?

21 Among others, Fuggles and Goldings are grown widely in Kent and Worcestershire. What are they?

22 What body of water lies off the south coast at Bournemouth?

23 Tintern Abbey was built in the 12th century near a river that forms the border between South Wales and England. What is the name of the river?

24 Which river, famed for its salmon, rises in the Cairngorm Mountains and flows east to the North Sea at Aberdeen?

25 What name is given to the famous prehistoric route between the English Channel and the centre of ancient Wessex that survives as minor roads or bridle paths?

22

1 Elton's first singles and albums were on the DJM label. What do the initials stand for?

2 With whom did Elton duet on the 1996 single 'Live Like Horses'?

3 Which 1974 single features members of The Beach Boys on backing vocals?

4 For which song did Elton and Tim Rice win the 1994 Academy Award?

5 What was Elton's first UK single release on his own Rocket label?

6 Who are the only two artists to have spent more weeks in the UK singles charts than Elton John?

7 Which other song was released on the single 'Candle in the Wind '97'?

8 Which album did Elton premiere at Wembley Stadium in June 1975?

9 What was Elton's first US number one single?

10 Which of Elton's albums was the biggest-selling album in the UK in 1973?

11 Which of Elton's singles was a tribute to a despatch rider killed in an accident?

12 Which American city did Elton sing about in a 1974 single?

13 On which album did the original recording of 'Candle in the Wind' first appear?

14 In the song 'Rocket Man', what time is 'zero hour'?

15 Who were the other three major artists featured on the 1985 charity single 'That's What Friends are For'?

16 With whom did Elton duet on 'Don't Go Breaking My Heart' in 1994?

17 Which 1982 single was written as a tribute to John Lennon?

18 On what occasion did Elton sing the hymn 'Abide with Me' at Wembley Stadium?

19 Which album features Elton's real name in its title?

20 Which song did Elton sing in the Ken Russell film of The Who's *Tommy*?

21 Which singer, later to release a live duet with Elton, featured uncredited on Elton's 1985 single 'Wrap Her Up'?

22 What type of venues did Elton play on his 2000 summer tour of Britain?

23 What was the title of Elton's 1973 Christmas single?

24 On which John Lennon single did Elton guest on piano and backing vocals?

25 What was Elton's first solo UK number one single?

1 What happened on 22 January 1901?

2 Who is the first female in line to the throne at present?

3 What relation was Kaiser Wilhelm II to King Edward VII?

4 Who was appointed chancellor of the University of London on the resignation of the Queen Mother in 1981?

5 How did 17-year-old Marcus Sergeant make the news in June 1981?

6 Who was created Chief Morning Star by Canada's Stormy Creek Indians in 1919?

7 Why was Edward VII's coronation put back from June to August in 1902?

8 Who owned Anmer, the horse under which suffragette Emily Davison threw herself at the 1913 Derby?

9 Lambert Simnel and Perkin Warbeck were pretenders to the throne of which king?

10 Which monarch had to wear leg splints as a child to combat knock-knees?

11 Aged fourteen and ten respectively, who spoke to the nation on the BBC's *Children's Hour* on 13 October 1940?

12 According to her wishes, in what colour was Queen Victoria dressed for her funeral?

13 Where did the royal version of the TV programme *It's a Knockout* take place?

14 Who served on board the HMS *Invincible* during the Falklands war?

15 What are Prince William's three middle names?

16 Which member of the royal family opened the 1956 Olympic Games in Melbourne?

17 Who was granted a *decree nisi* in Ipswich on 27 October 1936?

18 Who broke into Buckingham Palace and spent ten minutes in the Queen's bedroom in July 1982?

19 Who was the first monarch to visit Russia?

20 Under which monarch did the family change its name to Windsor?

21 Where did Diana visit on her first overseas tour as Princess of Wales in 1983?

22 Of which school was Prince Charles made head boy in January 1967?

23 Where did Princess Margaret marry photographer Antony Armstrong-Jones in May 1960?

24 Which member of the royal family participated in the 1926 Wimbledon men's doubles?

25 By which of his seven Christian names was Edward VIII usually called by his family?

9

1 Who was the first long jumper to exceed 29 feet?

2 What event occurred at Chamonix, at the foot of Mont Blanc, in 1924?

3 Who was the first British footballer to be transferred for £1 million?

4 Who was the first snooker player to score a maximum 147 break in the world championships?

5 Which British racing driver was the first man to win the Indianapolis 500 at the first attempt in 1966?

6 What was significant about the 1968 Olympic men's 100 metres final?

7 Cuban high jumper Javier Sotomayor was the first to better which key height in the event?

8 Who, in 1964, became the first Manchester United player to be voted European Footballer of the Year?

9 Who was the first unseeded player to win the men's singles title at Wimbledon?

10 Who was the first woman to officiate at a Football League fixture?

11 Which two teams contested the first Wembley FA Cup final?

12 Who were the first winners of the Rugby Union World Cup in 1987?

13 In the 1996 Atlanta games 400-metre hurdler Deon Hemmings became the first woman from which country to win an Olympic gold medal?

14 Who was the first man to run the 5,000 metres in under thirteen minutes?

15 In 1967 Keith Peacock of Charlton Athletic became the first Football League player to do what?

16 In which sporting event was Oxford student Sue Brown the first of her sex to participate in 1981?

17 At which women's event was Moroccan Nawal el Moutawakel the first Olympic champion in 1984?

18 In which year was the European Cup-Winners Cup first contested?

19 When Jonathan Edwards broke the world triple jump record in 1995 he did so twice in successive jumps. The first took him over the 18 metre mark; what 'milestone' was achieved with the second?

20 What was American Gertrude Ederle's achievement in 1926, bettering any previous performance by a man?

21 In which season did Manchester United first achieve the double?

22 Which American football team won the first Superbowl in 1967?

23 Who was the first black footballer to play in a senior international for Sweden?

24 Who was the first man to pole vault over 19 feet?

25 In 1780 jockey Sam Arnull rode Diomed to victory in the first running of which horse race?

1 Who was the star of the show *Ray's a Laugh*?

2 First broadcast in 1951, what did *Crazy People* go on to become?

3 Who were the two original stars of the show *Bandwagon*?

4 What did the initials stand for in the show *ITMA*?

5 Who was the subject of that show's title?

6 What was the ventriloquist's name in the 1950s series *Educating Archie*?

7 Which actor/comedian starred in *Variety Bandbox* as a spiv?

8 What was the name of Christopher Morris's radio news spoof which gave rise to the TV series *The Day Today*?

9 What was the full name of the occupant of 23 Railway Cuttings, East Cheam?

10 Which former members of *The Mary Whitehouse Experience* star in *The Now Show*?

11 What was Mrs Mopp's best-known catchphrase on the *ITMA* shows?

12 Which section of BBC radio started on 29 July 1945?

13 At which mythical RAF base were Richard Murdoch and Kenneth Horne teamed?

14 Which comedy duo, renowned for their later TV appearances, starred in *Laughter Incorporated* in 1958?

15 Which 'antidote to panel games' is hosted by Humphrey Lyttelton?

16 Who was the regular female member of the *Round the Horne* team?

17 Which show ran for thirteen series between 1959 and 1977, featuring among its cast Leslie Phillips, Jon Pertwee, Michael Bates and Ronnie Barker?

18 Who came to prominence as Archie Andrews' teacher, with the catchphrase 'Flippin' kids'?

19 Which show had episodes entitled 'The Nadger Plague', 'Who is Pink Oboe?' and 'The Toothpaste Expedition'?

20 Who was scriptwriter on *Educating Archie*, later to write and star in his own TV series?

21 Who is the host of *Just a Minute*?

22 Who played the camp duo Julian and Sandy in *Round the Horne*?

23 Which Australian and South African performers played regular supporting roles in *Hancock's Half Hour*?

24 Which family were introduced to the nation in the early 1950s on the show *Take It From Here*?

25 Which TV spoof chat show host started life as a spoof radio sports correspondent?

1 In which century was Alfred the Great king of the West Saxons?

2 What relation was George III to George II?

3 Which king of England was killed while hunting in the New Forest in 1100?

4 Whose death warrant was signed by Elizabeth I at Greenwich on 1 February 1587?

5 Who was monarch at the time of Archbishop of Canterbury Thomas à Becket's murder?

6 How old was Henry III when he came to the throne in 1216?

7 What was the family name of Robert I of Scotland?

8 Who became king in 1422 at less than nine months old?

9 At whose coronation was Handel's anthem 'Zadok the Priest' first performed in 1727?

10 Who was king of the Scots from 1040 to 1057?

11 Who was the last Tudor monarch of England?

12 Which of Henry VIII's wives was the mother of Queen Mary I?

13 When James VI of Scotland became James I of England in 1603, for how long had he occupied the Scottish throne?

14 Which monarch died from smallpox in 1694, at the age of thirty-two?

15 Which king suffered from the illness porphyria?

16 Who was the longest-reigning British monarch?

17 Which family of monarchs reigned after the Normans and before the House of Lancaster?

18 Who was on the throne at the time of the Great Fire of London?

19 Which king of England seized Normandy from his brother, Robert, in 1106 and imprisoned him for life?

20 Between 1340 and 1360, and again from 1369 to 1377, which monarch asserted his claim to the French throne?

21 Which two of Henry VIII's wives outlived him?

22 What is the relationship of princes William and Harry to Queen Victoria?

23 Where in July 1969 was Prince Charles invested as Prince of Wales?

24 Mary I and Elizabeth I were half-sisters. Who were the only sisters to be queens of England?

25 Who deposed his twelve-year-old nephew Edward V to become king in 1483?

1566

ANSWERS TO QUIZ 8

Famous Britons
1 Gareth Edwards
2 William Shakespeare
3 Daniel Lambert
4 Florence Nightingale
5 Bobby Charlton
6 Jayne and Christopher
7 Nicholas Montsarrat
8 Their first name is James
9 Bob Hoskins
10 Horatio Nelson
11 Winston Churchill
12 1976
13 Turner
14 Baby Spice
15 Denis Norden
16 Barry John
17 Bob Champion
18 Lord Kitchener
19 Stewart Granger
20 Laurence Olivier
21 Angela Mortimer
22 Bamber Gascoigne
23 Cameron Mackintosh
24 Guy Gibson
25 Jackie Stewart

British Comedies
1 Will Hay
2 George Cole
3 'Hot Stuff'
4 Rhys Ifans
5 The People's Front of Judaea
6 *The Ladykillers*
7 *The Importance of Being Earnest*
8 Dennis Price
9 *The Rebel*
10 Rick Mayall
11 Cast into models of the Eiffel Tower
12 Ronnie Corbett
13 *The League of Gentlemen*
14 *Secrets and Lies*
15 Alec Guinness
16 Simon Callow
17 Richard Griffiths
18 Alastair Sim
19 Peter Cook and Dudley Moore
20 Graham Chapman
21 George Formby
22 *School for Scoundrels*
23 John and Roy Boulting
24 *Shallow Grave*
25 Dirk Bogarde

The British Isles
1 Brecon Beacons National Park
2 Bala
3 Boyne
4 Stour
5 Loch Lomond
6 A mountain range in Ireland
7 The Old Man of Hoy (a column of rock)
8 Isle of Wight
9 Cannock Chase
10 Cheviot Hills
11 Guernsey
12 Isle of Man
13 Inner Hebrides
14 Cape Wrath
15 Anglesey
16 Tees
17 Mendips
18 The Norfolk Broads
19 Yorkshire Dales
20 Straits of Dover
21 Hops
22 Poole Bay
23 A canal
24 River Dee
25 Pilgrim's Way

Elton John
1 Dick James Music
2 Luciano Pavarotti
3 'Don't Let the Sun Go Down on Me'
4 'Can You Feel the Love Tonight'
5 'Don't Go Breaking My Heart', duet with Kiki Dee
6 Elvis Presley and Cliff Richard
7 'Something About the Way You Look Tonight'
8 *Captain Fantastic and the Brown Dirt Cowboy*
9 'Crocodile Rock', 1973
10 *Don't Shoot Me, I'm Only the Piano Player*
11 'Song for Guy'
12 Philadelpia
13 *Goodbye Yellow Brick Road*
14 9 am
15 Dionne Warwick, Gladys Knight and Stevie Wonder
16 RuPaul
17 'Empty Garden'
18 Before the 1984 FA Cup final (along with everyone else)
19 *Reg Strikes Back*, 1988
20 'Pinball Wizard'
21 George Michael
22 Stately homes
23 'Step Into Christmas'
24 'Whatever Gets You Through the Night'
25 'Sacrifice/Healing Hands'

The Royal Family
1 Queen Victoria died
2 Princess Beatrice, 5th in line altogether
3 Nephew
4 Princess Anne
5 He fired six blanks at the Queen during the Trooping of the Colour parade
6 The Prince of Wales, later Edward VIII
7 He had emergency surgery for appendicitis
8 King George V
9 Henry VII
10 George VI
11 Princesses Elizabeth and Margaret
12 White
13 Alton Towers theme park
14 Prince Andrew
15 Arthur Philip Louis
16 Prince Philip
17 Wallis Simpson
18 Michael Fagen
19 Edward VII, 1908
20 George V, 1917
21 Australia and New Zealand
22 Gordonstoun
23 Westminster Abbey
24 The Duke of York, later George VI
25 David

Sporting Firsts
1 Bob Beamon
2 The first Winter Olympic Games
3 Trevor Francis
4 Cliff Thorburn
5 Graham Hill
6 It was the first all-black Olympic sprint final
7 8 feet
8 Denis Law
9 Boris Becker
10 Wendy Toms
11 Bolton Wanderers and West Ham United
12 New Zealand
13 Jamaica
14 Said Aouita
15 Substitute another player
16 The University Boat Race
17 400-metre hurdles
18 1960
19 The first jump over 60 feet
20 She was the first woman to swim the English Channel
21 1993/94
22 Green Bay Packers
23 Martin Dahlin
24 Scotland and England
25 The Derby

Radio Comedy
1 Ted Ray
2 *The Goon Show*
3 Arthur Askey and Richard Murdoch
4 *It's That Man Again*
5 Adolf Hitler
6 Peter Brough
7 Arthur English
8 *On the Hour*
9 Anthony Aloysius StJohn Hancock
10 Hugh Dennis and Steve Punt
11 'Can I do you now, Sir?'
12 The Light Programme
13 *Much Binding in the Marsh*
14 Morecambe and Wise
15 *I'm Sorry I Haven't a Clue*
16 Betty Marsden
17 *The Navy Lark*
18 Tony Hancock
19 *The Goon Show*
20 Eric Sykes
21 Nicholas Parsons
22 Hugh Paddick and Kenneth Williams
23 Bill Kerr and Sid James
24 The Glums
25 Alan Partridge

British Monarchs
1 The ninth
2 Grandson
3 William II
4 Mary, Queen of Scots
5 Henry II
6 Nine
7 Bruce
8 Henry VI
9 George II
10 Macbeth
11 Elizabeth I
12 Catherine of Aragon
13 Almost thirty-six years
14 Mary II
15 George III
16 Victoria (June 1837 to January 1901)
17 The Plantagenets
18 Charles II
19 Henry I
20 Edward III
21 Anne of Cleves and Catherine Parr
22 Great-great-great-great-grandsons
23 Caernarfon Castle
24 Mary II and Anne
25 Richard III

THE GREATEST TRIVIA QUIZ BOOK

QUIZ 9

1 Which famous silver screen act made their debut in 1929's *The Cocoanuts*?

2 Which American president married his cousin?

3 What was the Christian name of the brother of writers Edith and Sacheverell Sitwell?

4 What name connects the actors Henry, Peter, Jane and Bridget?

5 Pope Alexander VI, who died in 1503, was a member of which family?

6 Which American athlete, himself an Olympic gold medallist at the 1984 games, was the husband of one 1988 gold medallist and brother of another?

7 Kristin shot JR in *Dallas*. The actress who played her had a famous singer as a father. Who was he?

8 What was the surname of French brothers Etienne and Joseph, who pioneered hot-air balloon flights in 1783?

9 Who was the actress sister of Olivia de Havilland?

10 What are the Christian names of the Australian cricket team's Waugh twins?

11 Which musical family rose to fame on Andy Williams' TV shows and had ten UK hits between 1972 and 1976?

12 Which family were grand dukes of Tuscany from 1569 to 1737?

13 How many brothers did the Brontë sisters have?

14 Which French father and son were, respectively, a painter and film director?

15 In which field are brothers Ridley and Tony Scott famous?

16 Which Barrymore is the odd one out from these: John, Ethel, Lionel, Drew and Michael?

17 Which American TV family was based on the *'Til Death Us Do Part* Garnett family, and featured Carrol O'Connor as Archie?

18 With which sport do you associate Fred Stolle and his son Sandon?

19 What is the surname of the actors Beau and Jeff and their late father, Lloyd?

20 From what did the royal family change its name to Windsor?

21 Which TV series launched the career of David Cassidy?

22 Which families are central to the story of Romeo and Juliet?

23 What is the name of the Viennese family associated with the waltz?

24 What was the family connection between singer Marvin Gaye and Motown boss Berry Gordy?

25 What were the Christian names of the parents of president John F Kennedy?

1 Which of the stars of *Easy Rider* also directed the movie?

2 What is the setting for Tod Browning's 1932 film *Freaks*?

3 Where does the finale of the final confrontation in *Enter the Dragon* take place?

4 Which statuesque actress walks through Rome's Trevi Fountain in Fellini's *La Dolce Vita*?

5 What did director Ridley Scott do with Harrison Ford's narration in *Blade Runner – The Director's Cut*?

6 Who played Hannibal Lecter in the 1986 film *Manhunter*, four years before *The Silence of the Lambs*?

7 In which Ken Russell film did Oliver Reed play the Jesuit-educated Father Grandier and Vanessa Redgrave a hunchbacked Mother Superior?

8 Which real-life comedian/actor is the kidnap victim in Martin Scorsese's *King of Comedy*?

9 Which flamboyant fashion designer was responsible for the costumes in Peter Greenaway's *The Cook, The Thief, His Wife and Her Lover*?

10 Terrence Malick's directorial debut in 1973 starred Martin Sheen and Sissy Spacek, on the run from the law. What was the film?

11 Which actor won an Academy Award for his role in *The Usual Suspects*?

12 Who played the title role in the 1963 film *The Servant*?

13 Which Mel Brooks film featured the 'Springtime for Hitler' routine?

14 In which film did Steve Martin recite the 'Pointy Birds' poem?

15 In which film does Edward Woodward star as a police sergeant investigating the disappearance of a twelve-year-old girl on a Scottish island?

16 Which Orson Welles film starts with a three-and-a-half-minute continuous shot of a bomb being planted in a car, and the car's subsequent fate?

17 In which 1961 film did Paul Newman play Fast Eddie Felson?

18 Which film features an eighteen-inch-high model of Stonehenge, Elvis Presley's grave, and an amplifier that 'goes up to eleven'?

19 Which 1974 film introduced a character called Leatherface?

20 Which film's action takes place in a warehouse after a bungled diamond robbery?

21 In which film were Brad Pitt and Morgan Freeman teamed as detectives on the trail of a serial killer?

22 Which 1986 film starred Richard E Grant and Paul McGann as a couple of out-of-work actors needing to get away from London to 'rejuvenate'?

23 Who wrote The Rocky Horror Show, from which came The Rocky Horror Picture Show?

24 Who played the title role in Betty Blue?

25 Which 1971 Stanley Kubrick film was given a new cinema and video release only after the death of the director?

24

A CLAUDIE OSSARD-JEAN-JACQUES BEINEIX PRODUCT

a Jean Jacques Beineix

Betty Blue

37°2 IN THE MORNIN

20

1 Which mountain overlooks the city of Naples?

2 Aconcagua is the highest mountain in South America. In which country does it stand?

3 By which city does the Sugar Loaf Mountain stand?

4 Which mountain range spans northern Morocco, Algeria and Tunisia?

5 In which country are the Sierra Madre ranges?

6 In which state is the USA's highest mountain, Mount McKinley?

7 In which country is Mount Ararat?

8 Mont Blanc stands on the border of which two European countries?

9 Why would it be incorrect to describe this mountain as Mount Fujiyama?

10 Which mountain in the Swiss Alps is featured in a Clint Eastwood film?

11 Which East African mountain has a Swahili name meaning 'mountain of the god of cold'?

12 Which Australian mountain was discovered by a Polish explorer and named after one of his countrymen?

13 Which mountain in the British Isles has a railway going to its summit?

14 Which mountain was named in 1865 after the British surveyor-general of India?

15 What does the word 'Ben' mean, as in Ben Nevis?

16 In which mountain range does the country of Andorra lie?

17 Mauna Kea is an extinct volcano on which Pacific island?

18 What is the name shared by mountains in Iceland and the Isle of Man?

19 In which state is the Mount Rushmore monument, featuring the faces of four presidents?

20 By what name do most of us know the peak the French call Mont Cervin and the Italians call Monte Cervino?

21 In which American state are the Adirondack Mountains?

22 In which country are the Apennines?

23 In which country is Mount Cook, named after explorer Captain James Cook?

24 In which mountain range is the ski resort of Aspen?

25 What is the name of the flat-topped mountain overlooking Cape Town in South Africa?

1 Which British producer worked in tandem with Madonna on her *Ray of Light* album?

2 Which country singer guested with the KLF on their single 'Justified and Ancient'?

3 The drum break from 'Funky Drummer' is one of the most-used samples of all time. Who recorded the original track?

4 Who was the owner of Manchester's Hacienda Club and Factory Records?

5 With which band did Norman Cook have a UK Number One in 1990?

6 Alex Gifford and Will White were joined by Shirley Bassey on their single 'History Repeating'. By what name are they known collectively?

7 What was the name of Shaun Ryder's post-Happy Mondays group?

8 Which British dance act was masterminded by Jazzie B and Nellee Hooper?

9 How are Ed Simons and Tom Rowlands better known?

10 With which Spice Girl did Missy 'Misdemeanor' Elliott sing on 'I Want You Back'?

11 Which techno artists' albums include *Accelerator*, *Lifeforms* and *Dead Cities*?

12 What was The Prodigy's first UK hit single?

13 Which female vocalist guested with Massive Attack on their third album, *Mezzanine*?

14 Which band named themselves after a milk drink featured in *A Clockwork Orange*?

15 Posdnous, Trugoy the Dove and P.A. Pasemaster Mase had their first hit in 1989. By what name are they collectively known?

16 'Ride On Time' spent six weeks at number 1 in the UK in 1989. For whom?

17 Which Detroit producer has used pseudonyms such as 69, Psyche, Paperclip People and Innerzone Orchestra?

18 Which singer made his first appearance on Adamski's 'Killer' in 1992?

19 From which US city did techno originate?

20 Which Chicago club gave house music its name?

21 Which DJ and recording artist is known as the 'House Godfather'?

22 Which Steve 'Silk' Hurley single was the first house record to top the UK charts in 1987?

23 Whose albums include *Better Living by Chemistry* and *You've Come a Long Way, Baby*?

24 Who released their second album *Rhythm and Stealth* in 1999?

25 Moby is a descendent of which famous author?

20

1 On which island did the worst air disaster occur in 1977, where two Boeing 747s collided, leaving 583 people dead?

2 Which oil tanker ran aground in Prince William Sound, Alaska, in 1989?

3 What disaster occurred on the night of April 14–15 1912?

4 What was the nature of the disaster at Bhopal, India, in December 1984, which claimed up to 3,000 lives?

5 In which country did the British airship R101 crash, killing fifty people in 1903?

6 Which Welsh village was devastated in 1966 when a huge volume of slurry slipped down into the village, engulfing the local school, killing 116 children and 28 adults?

7 Between 1918 and 1920, more than 21.5 million lives were claimed in an epidemic of which illness?

8 In which of the United States is Mount St Helens, which erupted in 1980?

9 What was the name of the Russian submarine that was flooded and stranded on the sea bed in August 2000?

10 What type of disaster occurred at Berlin in 1908, Brooklyn, New York in 1918 and Balham, London in 1940?

11 In which year did the *Torrey Canyon* run aground off the Scilly Isles, spilling its 120,000 tonnes of oil?

12 St Pierre, the capital of Martinique in the West Indies, was completely wiped out in 1902. What caused this catastrophe?

13 At which motor racing event in 1955 were eighty-two people killed when a Mercedes-Benz 300 SLR went out of control, exploded and showered wreckage into the crowd?

14 Which American city was devastated by earthquake and fire in April 1906?

15 In which year did the explosion of the Chernobyl nuclear reactor occur?

16 Off the coast of which African country did the tanker *Castillo de Belver* catch fire and split in two in August 1983?

17 At which Scottish football ground did sixty-six people die when barriers buckled and collapsed at the end of a game in January 1971?

18 What was the cause of twenty-nine deaths at the village of Flixborough, Humberside, on 2 June 1974?

19 From which Belgian port did the ferry *Herald of Free Enterprise* set sail on 6 March 1987 before letting in water and capsizing?

20 Which Zeppelin caught fire at Lakehurst, New Jersey, on 6 May 1937?

21 Which military disaster of the Crimean War did Tennyson famously mourn in verse?

22 What struck Central America in 1998, killing nearly 10,000 people and leaving approximately 2.5 million people dependent on aid?

23 Which American state penitentiary caught fire in 1930, resulting in 322 deaths?

24 At which British airport did fifty-four people perish when a Boeing 737 engine exploded before takeoff in August 1985?

25 In which year was the Lockerbie disaster, which destroyed Pan Am flight 103, killing 270 people?

1 Five-time world squash champion Susan Devoy came from which country?

2 Which American tennis player won all 26 of her singles matches in Wightman Cup competitions against Britain between 1971 and 1985?

3 Who won the 100 metres at the 1984 Olympics in a then world record time?

4 Who won the javelin gold medal for Britain at the same games?

5 At which sport did Italian Deborah Compagnioni win Olympic gold medals at each of the games in 1992, 1994 and 1998?

6 Who won Australia's 100th Olympic gold medal of all time during the Sydney games?

7 Who won gold for Britain in the 1991 World Championships in Tokyo in the 10,000 metres?

8 Czech Vera Caslavska won seven Olympic titles in all in 1964 and 1968. What was her sport?

9 With which sport do you associate Australian Karrie Webb?

10 Who won the Wimbledon singles title at the age of nineteen in 1971 and again nine years later after she had married and become a mother?

11 Which South African-born runner competed for Britain barefoot at the 1984 Olympics?

12 Which sprinter took part in the Moscow games of 1980 and was still competing at the highest level in Sydney?

13 Who won silver for Britain in the judo competition at Sydney?

14 Which Australian swimmer won Olympic gold medals in the 100 metres freestyle in 1956, 1960 and 1964?

15 How many Grand Slam titles has Steffi Graf won?

16 Who won gold at the 1987 and 1991 World Athletics Championships in the long jump and in 1993 and 1997 in the heptathlon?

17 What year saw the Wall Street Crash?

18 At what sport did Hungarian Krisztina Egerszegi win Olympic gold in 1988 at the age of fourteen?

19 Who won the French Open women's singles tennis championship in 2000?

20 Who did the 100 and 200 metres sprint double in Sydney?

21 The winner of the 1971 European Three-Day Event was also voted BBC Sports Personality of the Year. Who was she?

22 With which sport do you associate American Picabo Street?

23 German Ulrike Meyfarth won gold at the 1972 Munich Olympics and repeated her triumph twelve years later in Los Angeles. What was her event?

24 Who was the last Briton to win the Wimbledon singles title before Virginia Wade in 1977?

25 Who was the first gymnast ever to score a perfect '10' at the Montreal Olympics of 1976?

15

1 In which town is *The Simpsons* set?

2 Who are Miss Hoover and Ms Krabappel?

3 What was Marge's maiden name?

4 Which character's 'real name' is Herschel Krustovsky?

5 At which exclusive club did Homer have his behind smacked with wooden paddles during his initiation ritual?

6 Which occasional character's voice is supplied by *Frasier* star Kelsey Grammer?

7 Who drives the school bus?

8 Who usually reads the news on the Simpsons' TV?

9 On whose real-life TV show did the Simpsons make their first appearance?

10 Lisa had a birthday song written for her by a guest in the Simpsons' home. Who was the guest pretending to be?

11 What is the full name of Homer's boss?

12 What is the name of Chief Wiggum's son?

13 Who was the founder of the town in which the Simpsons live?

14 When Bart went on an exchange trip to France what did he see the wine makers adding to the wine?

15 Which character is nicknamed 'Spanky' by his mother?

16 Who was the inspiration for the voice of Mayor Quimby?

17 Who played the voice of Homer's half-brother, Herb?

18 Which grown man collects Malibu Stacy dolls?

19 Who is Santa's Little Helper?

20 Of what type of public vehicle did Homer become a driver?

21 On which tough-guy actor's voice did Hank Azaria base that of Chief Wiggum?

22 Whom did Barney Gumble replace in the barbershop quartet, The B Sharps?

23 What is Homer's father's first name?

24 Which of Burns and Smithers is voiced by Harry Shearer?

25 During a game of which sport did Bart and Lisa make up after they had fallen out?

1 Which city was besieged by the Turks in 1453?

2 After the United States, which country supplied the most troops to fight Iraq in the Gulf War in 1991?

3 How many ships were in the Spanish Armada of 1588?

4 At which battle did the Americans, led by Major-General Horatio Coates, defeat the British under Lt General Sir John Burgoyne in 1777?

5 Whom did the Japanese defeat at the Battle of Tsushima in 1905?

6 Who led the Macedonians against the Persians at the Battle of Gaugamela in 331 BC?

7 Whose brothers, Gyrth and Leofwine, fought at the Battle of Hastings in 1066?

8 At the Battle of Blenheim in 1704, who led the allied troops against the French?

9 At which sea battle did the Americans defeat the Japanese in 1942, despite their ships being outnumbered three to one?

10 During which war did the Battle of Agincourt take place?

11 Who were the Duke of Wellington's and Napoleon's respective co-commanders at the Battle of Waterloo?

12 Which battle was fought between the Union and Confederate armies from 1–3 July 1863?

13 Who led the Israelis in the Sinai campaign against Egypt at the time of the Suez crisis?

14 Who was the Japanese commander at the Battle of Singapore in 1942?

15 Where, in September 1950, did General MacArthur's troops land prior to the recapture of Seoul?

16 Which man led the British, Portuguese and Sepoys against the Bengalis at Plassey in 1757?

17 Who put Vienna under siege in 1529?

18 Where did Cromwell's New Model Army defeat the Royalists in 1651 to end the Civil War?

19 Which of the Solomon Islands was regained from the Japanese by the Americans in May 1942?

20 Who became King of England after the Battle of Bosworth Field in 1485?

21 Which battle against the Austrians and the Russians in 1805 is regarded as Napoleon's greatest victory?

22 Who led the Americans to victory against the British at Princeton in 1777?

23 Who inspired the French to resist the English at Orléans in 1429?

24 Who was head of RAF Fighter Command at the Battle of Britain?

25 Which English king was defeated by the Scots at the Battle of Bannockburn in 1314?

ANSWERS TO QUIZ 9

Famous Families
1 The Marx Brothers
2 Franklin D Roosevelt
3 Osbert
4 Fonda
5 The Borgias
6 Al Joyner
7 Bing Crosby
8 Montgolfier
9 Joan Fontaine
10 Steve and Mark
11 The Osmonds
12 The Medicis
13 One
14 Pierre Auguste Renoir and Jean Renoir
15 Film direction
16 Michael; the others are all part of the American acting family
17 The Bunkers
18 Tennis
19 Bridges
20 Saxe-Coburg-Gotha
21 The Partridge Family
22 The Montagues and the Capulets
23 Strauss
24 Gaye married Gordy's sister, Anna
25 Joseph and Rose

Cult Films
1 Dennis Hopper
2 A circus
3 In a hall of mirrors
4 Anita Ekberg
5 He removed it
6 Brian Cox
7 *The Devils*
8 Jerry Lewis
9 Jean Paul Gaultier
10 *Badlands*
11 Kevin Spacey
12 Dirk Bogarde
13 *The Producers*
14 *The Man with Two Brains*
15 *The Wicker Man*
16 *Touch of Evil*
17 *The Hustler*
18 *This is Spinal Tap*
19 *The Texas Chain Saw Massacre*
20 *Reservoir Dogs*
21 *Se7en*
22 *Withnail and I*
23 Richard O'Brien
24 Béatrice Dalle
25 *A Clockwork Orange*

Mountains
1 Mount Vesuvius
2 Argentina
3 Rio de Janeiro
4 The Atlas Mountains
5 Mexico
6 Alaska
7 Turkey
8 France and Italy
9 Yama means 'mountain', so it should be Fujiyama or Mount Fuji
10 The Eiger
11 Kilimanjaro
12 Mount Kosciusko
13 Snowdon
14 Everest, after Sir George Everest
15 Mountain
16 The Pyrenees
17 Hawaii
18 Snaefell
19 South Dakota
20 The Matterhorn
21 New York
22 Italy
23 New Zealand
24 The Rocky Mountains
25 Table Mountain

Dance Music
1 William Orbit
2 Tammy Wynette
3 James Brown
4 Tony Wilson
5 Beats International
6 Propellerheads
7 Black Grape
8 Soul II Soul
9 Chemical Brothers
10 Mel B/Scary Spice
11 Future Sound of London
12 'Charly'
13 Elizabeth Fraser
14 Moloko
15 De La Soul
16 Black Box
17 Carl Craig
18 Seal
19 Detroit
20 The Warehouse Club
21 Frankie Knuckles
22 'Jack Your Body'
23 Fatboy Slim
24 Leftfield
25 Herman Melville

Disasters
1 Tenerife
2 The *Exxon Valdez*
3 The sinking of the *Titanic*
4 The Union Carbide plant leaked poisonous gas
5 France
6 Aberfan
7 Influenza
8 Washington
9 The *Kursk*
10 Underground rail disasters

11 1967
12 Volcanic eruption
13 Le Mans
14 San Francisco
15 1986
16 South Africa
17 1929
18 An explosion at a chemical plant
19 Zeebrugge
20 The *Hindenburg*
21 The Charge of the Light Brigade
22 Hurricane Mitch
23 Ohio
24 Manchester
25 1988

Sportswomen
1 New Zealand
2 Chris Evert
3 Evelyn Ashford
4 Tessa Sanderson
5 Slalom skiing
6 Cathy Freeman
7 Liz McColgan
8 Gymnastics
9 Golf
10 Evonne Cawley née Goolagong
11 Zola Budd
12 Merlene Ottey
13 Dawn Fraser
14 Kate Howey
15 22
16 Jackie Joyner-Kersee
17 Hockey
18 Swimming (200 m backstroke)
19 Mary Pierce
20 Marion Jones
21 Princess Anne
22 Skiing
23 High jump
24 Ann Jones, 1969
25 Nadia Comaneci

The Simpsons
1 Springfield
2 Lisa's and Bart's schoolteachers
3 Bouvier
4 Krusty the Klown
5 The Stonecutters
6 Sideshow Bob
7 Otto
8 Kent Brockman
9 Tracey Ullman
10 Michael Jackson (who provided the voice)
11 Charles Montgomery Burns
12 Ralph
13 Jebediah Springfield
14 Antifreeze
15 Principal Seymour Skinner
16 John F Kennedy
17 Danny DeVito
18 Waylon Smithers
19 The Simpsons' dog
20 The monorail
21 Edward G Robinson
22 Chief Wiggum
23 Abraham
24 Both
25 Ice hockey

Famous Battles
1 Constantinople
2 Saudi Arabia
3 130
4 Saratoga
5 The Russians
6 Alexander the Great
7 King Harold II's
8 The Duke of Marlborough and Prince Eugene of Savoy
9 The Battle of Midway
10 The Hundred Years' War
11 Field Marshal Blucher and Marshal Ney
12 The Battle of Gettysburg
13 Moshe Dayan
14 General Yamashita
15 Inchon
16 Robert Clive
17 The Turks
18 Worcester
19 Guadalcanal
20 Henry Tudor (Henry VII)
21 Austerlitz
22 George Washington
23 Joan of Arc
24 Air Chief Marshal Sir Hugh Dowding
25 Edward II

THE GREATEST TRIVIA QUIZ BOOK

QUIZ 10

25

1 Who did Lauren Bacall marry after the death of Humphrey Bogart?

2 Catherine of Aragon was a widow when she married Henry VIII. Who was her first husband?

3 By today's standards, Cleopatra's marriage to Mark Antony was bigamous and her first marriage would have been frowned on. Who was her first husband?

4 Who was the comic partner of the man born Arthur Jefferson?

5 Leofric, Earl of Mercia, was married to a woman famous for an act of protest. What was her name?

6 Shakira Baksh is married to which screen superstar?

7 Which pop songwriting couple were behind the hits 'Will You Love Me Tomorrow?' and 'Do The Loco-Motion'?

8 In which year did Queen Victoria marry Prince Albert of Saxe-Coburg-Gotha?

9 *Tristram and Isolde* is an opera by which composer?

10 He was once a British monarch; she once ran a hotel. Which British acting couple?

11 'Sock it to me!' girl Judy Carne was the first and Loni Anderson the second wife of which film star?

12 Which duo, who became Universal's top box-office draw in the 1940s, made their film debut in 1940's *One Night in the Tropics*?

13 Which year saw the divorce between Diana, Princess of Wales and Prince Charles?

14 Who was Frank Sinatra's third wife?

15 Anne Hayes, Britt Ekland, Miranda Quarry and Lynn Frederick were the four wives of which comedian and actor?

16 Ronnie Bennett was married to which famous record producer?

17 Who are actress Jamie Lee Curtis's famous parents?

18 What were the surnames of the men who discovered insulin?

19 Who was married to Adolf Hitler for one day?

20 'Nutbush City Limits' was a hit for which troubled couple?

21 Which famous couple was the subject of an opera by Engelbert Humperdinck?

22 Which famous partnership called their circus 'The Greatest Show on Earth'?

23 Which famous writer, author of *The Second Sex*, was the partner of Jean-Paul Sartre?

24 Sir David Frost was once married to which of the four ladies mentioned in question 15?

25 Who is the film producer/director husband of Julie Andrews?

1 The characters Charlie Allnutt and Rose Sayer were an unlikely romantic couple in which 1951 classic?

2 Frank Farmer (a former Secret Service agent) and Rachel Marron (a pop superstar) fall in love in which 1992 movie?

3 Melanie Griffith, John Goodman and Don Johnson reprise the roles first played by Judy Holliday, Broderick Crawford and William Holden in a 1993 remake of which 1950 romantic comedy?

4 Which famous romance begins with Dr Alec Harvey removing a cinder from Laura Jesson's eye at a railway station?

5 Marlee Matlin plays an intelligent but isolated young woman, working as a janitor in a school for the deaf, with whom a new teacher falls in love. What is the title of the movie?

6 Charlie Chaplin's last film starred Marlon Brando and Sophia Loren as the romantic leads. What was it called?

7 Which story of a romance between an American soldier and a British nurse has been made into a movie twice, starring Gary Cooper and Helen Hayes in 1932 and Rock Hudson and Jennifer Jones in 1957?

8 Mel Gibson plays Daniel and Jamie Lee Curtis is Claire in which romantic fantasy involving cryogenics?

9 A lonely widow is romanced by the ghost of an English sea captain in which 1947 comedy that inspired a 1970s TV series?

10 Which Steve Martin romantic comedy of 1991 has Harris (a TV weatherman) finally pairing up with Sara (a journalist)?

11 Which 1982 romance takes place around a US Naval Aviation Officer Candidate School?

12 Which courtroom battle of the sexes starred real-life couple Spencer Tracy and Katharine Hepburn in 1949?

13 Which 1985 romantic drama sees Robert Redford woo Meryl Streep?

14 'Two professional Mafia killers meet, fall in love, marry, and find out that the mob may not be big enough for both of them' describes which black comedy of 1985?

15 Which romantic couple have been played over the years by Sean Connery and Audrey Hepburn, Errol Flynn and Olivia de Havilland, and Richard Todd and Joan Rice?

16 Which romantic adventure first paired Michael Douglas and Kathleen Turner as a pair of disaster-prone lovers?

17 In which 1987 reworking of the story of Cyrano de Bergerac does Steve Martin play a small town fire chief in love with Darryl Hannah?

18 Barley Blair and Katya are the lovers in which movie based on a John Le Carré novel of the same name?

19 Which 1993 biographical drama told the story of C S Lewis's love for poet Joy Gresham?

20 In which film do Robert Redford and Barbra Streisand dress up as Groucho and Harpo Marx in a party scene?

21 Which 1989 romantic comedy directed by Rob Reiner tells the story of two people who take thirteen years to fall in love?

22 Tess tells Jack 'I have a head for business and a bod for sin' in which 1988 romantic comedy?

23 Which romantic adventure, set in 1960s Indonesia, stars Mel Gibson and Sigourney Weaver?

24 Which 1961 movie, written and directed by Peter Ustinov, tells the love story of the children of US and Russian ambassadors to Italy?

25 What was the title of the 1976 sequel to the weepie *Love Story*?

1

1 Which common flower has the scientific name *bellis perennis* and has a connection, through song, with a bicycle?

2 Where do hydrophytic plants grow?

3 What would you find in the pods of the *pisum stativum*?

4 At three feet in diameter the rafflesia has the largest single flower of any plant in the world. In which part of the world does it grow?

5 How do procumbent plants grow?

6 What word is used to describe bell-shaped flowers?

7 In what conditions do thermophilous plants thrive?

8 What is meant by the name of saxifrage, which grows in cracks in rocks?

9 Where does bracket fungus grow?

10 Which carnivorous plant's natural habitat consists of a small coastal area between North and South Carolina?

11 Where does the edelweiss grow?

12 What colour is the flower of the Amazon lily when it opens?

13 What is the more common name of the poisonous plant *atropa belladonna*?

14 Where is the natural habitat of the cheese plant?

15 Which family of plants sends up shoots in the shape of croziers?

16 What trick does the mirror orchid play on a male bee?

17 Which shrub was introduced to England in 1598, can be used in cooking, and is also a component of Eau de Cologne?

18 From which country did the leek originate?

19 What would you be most likely to be chewing if it were flavoured with *mentha piperita* or *mentha viridis*?

20 Botanists, gardeners and chefs know their *allium cepas*. What is an *allium cepa*?

21 What is another name for the white poppy?

22 What name is given to a plant that grows from seed, and that flowers and dies within a year?

23 Which flower is represented on the flag of India?

24 What type of plant is a lady's slipper?

25 Swedish botanist Anders Dahl gave his name to which flower?

1 In which town was Elvis born on 8 January 1935?

2 Which two songs were on Elvis's first single on the Sun label in the United States?

3 What was the name of Elvis's vocal backing group?

4 What was Elvis's first UK hit?

5 Which guitarist and bass player accompanied Elvis on his first recording session, and on many subsequent sessions?

6 What was Elvis's first feature film?

7 Prior to his posthumous number one, 'Way Down', what was Elvis's last UK chart-topping single?

8 In which city did Elvis marry Priscilla Beaulieu on 1 May 1967?

9 What was the name of Elvis's twin brother, who was stillborn?

10 What is the significance of the number US53310761?

11 Which songwriting team was responsible for such hits as 'Hound Dog', '(You're So Square) Baby I Don't Care', 'Trouble' and 'King Creole'?

12 How much did RCA pay Sun for Elvis's recording contract in November 1955?

13 What event happened on 1 February 1968?

14 Which Elvis song was based on the German folk song 'Muss Ich Denn Zum Stadtele Hinaus'?

15 What links Dr John Carpenter, Guy Lambert, Danny Fisher, Walter Gulick and Lt Josh Morgan?

16 Whom did Elvis receive as guests at his Beverley Hills home on 27 August 1965?

17 Who played Elvis in Elvis: The Movie in 1979?

18 What was Elvis's first UK number one single?

19 Which Elvis single had two spells at the top of the UK charts in 1965?

20 By what name was Dutchman Andreas Cornelius van Kuijk better known?

21 In the song 'Trouble', what does Elvis say is his middle name?

22 In which two consecutive years did Elvis score four UK number one hit singles?

23 Which United States president made Elvis a special agent of the Bureau of Narcotics and Dangerous Drugs?

24 Who, along with Elvis, made up the 'Million Dollar Quartet'?

25 In the song 'Jailhouse Rock', which instrument is played by Spider Murphy?

9

1 Which year saw the maiden flight of a US Space Shuttle?

2 The Bay of Pigs was very much in the news in 1961. Where is it located?

3 In January 1971 President Milton Obote of Uganda was overthrown by his army commander. What was his name?

4 What sports event happened at Iffley Road, Oxford, on 6 May 1954?

5 Who was found dead in a bungalow near Hollywood on 5 August 1962?

6 In which year did the Chernobyl nuclear disaster take place?

7 Where were four men with electronic surveillance equipment arrested at gunpoint in June 1972?

8 What 200-page document was signed on 28 June 1919?

9 Where is the prison in which Nelson Mandela was held from 1964 to 1990?

10 How did a group called 'Black September' make headlines in 1972?

11 1988 saw the appointment of the first woman prime minister in the Islamic world. Who was she?

12 What event of 1963 was captured on the most famous, and most valuable, piece of amateur film footage ever shot?

13 Who were the targets of a terrorist bomb at Brighton's Grand Hotel in 1984?

14 What is being attacked in the picture below?

15 In which year did Alaska and Hawaii become the 49th and 50th states of the Union?

16 Which high-profile politician was caught on video, crackpipe in hand, by the FBI in 1990?

17 What was opened at Luxor, Egypt, in February 1924?

18 American Terry Anderson was taken hostage in Lebanon in 1984. What year was he released?

19 What happened at Cheddington, Buckinghamshire, on 8 August 1963?

20 Which American politician was shot and paralysed by Arthur Bremer in 1972?

21 Which former Viceroy of India was murdered by a terrorist bomb in August 1979?

22 In which state is the Three Mile Island nuclear power plant, scene of a near-disaster in 1979?

23 By what name has Monday 19 October 1987 come to be remembered ?

24 Which New York building was damaged by a bomb in 1983?

25 What was the name of the Salman Rushdie book, the publication of which brought about the Islamic death threat and forced him into hiding?

5

1 Which Frenchman, born in 1871, was synonymous with the World Cup?

2 Which country hosted the first World Cup in 1930?

3 What was significant about Rob Rensenbrink's goal for Holland against Scotland in the 1978 World Cup?

4 What connects Tunisian Mr Ali Bennaceur to England's exit from the 1986 World Cup quarterfinal?

5 Against which team did Pele score three goals in the 1958 semifinal?

6 What did teams use for the first time at the World Cup in Mexico in 1970?

7 How many goals did Gary Lineker score in World Cup final stages?

8 Which two teams were victorious on the first day of the first World Cup in 1930?

9 Which was the first final to go into extra time?

10 The infamous clash between Chile and Italy in 1962 has gone down in history – what is it known as?

11 For which country did Said Owarian score a sensational individual goal against Belgium in the 1994 tournament?

12 Stuart Pearce and Chris Waddle are remembered for their penalty misses in the 1990 semifinal shoot-out against West Germany, but which three Englishmen scored from the spot?

13 Which was the first African nation to reach the final stages?

14 Michael Owen scored a stunning second goal for England against Argentina in the 1998 tournament. Who scored England's first goal in the match proper?

15 Who scored the most goals in a single tournament?

16 Who was Scotland's manager in the 1978 competition in Argentina?

17 Which Brazilian scored in every round of the 1970 World Cup?

18 Who was top scorer in the 1966 competition held in England?

19 Which country was beaten 9-0 by Yugoslavia in the 1974 tournament?

20 Against whom did Pele score his first goal in the final stages of a World Cup, in 1958?

21 Which was the first country to win a World Cup on home soil?

22 Who scored West Germany's last-minute equaliser in the 1966 final against England?

23 In which Californian city was the 1994 final played?

24 Which was the first team to be eliminated from a World Cup without losing a match?

25 1998 was the second time that France hosted the World Cup. Which two other countries have also hosted it twice?

1 What false name is used by the con man in the first episode?

2 In which seaside town is the series based?

3 Where is Basil trying to get to when his car breaks down?

4 What is the name of the French restaurant owner who comes to Basil's rescue on gourmet night?

5 Which regular character joined the hotel in the second series?

6 What is the name of the builder that Sybil wants to do the work in the hotel?

7 With whom does Basil see Polly in an embrace, from which he totally misinterprets the situation?

8 What is the name of the horse on which Basil places a bet?

9 In his muddled conversation with the deaf Mrs Richards, where does Manuel tell her that Basil comes from?

10 Which regular character is played by Ballard Berkeley?

11 What is the name of the hotel on which John Cleese and Connie Booth based *Fawlty Towers*, which actually gets mentioned in the episode with the builders?

12 What are the names of the hotel's two elderly lady residents?

13 Which member of the show's cast appeared in the 1954 David Lean film *Hobson's Choice*?

14 What falls onto Basil's head in the episode with the Germans?

15 What is Manuel's birthday present from Basil?

16 Who plays the spoon salesman who Basil mistakes for a hotel inspector?

17 Into whom does Basil threaten to insert a garden gnome?

18 Who plays the role of the doctor in the episode with the corpse?

19 What does Basil put rat poison on in the episode with the health inspector?

20 Who announces, rather grandly, 'I know nothing'?

21 What is poking out of the top of Basil's pullover when the doctor comes into the dead man's room?

22 Which composer's music does Sybil describe as a 'racket'?

23 How does Basil get out of the hotel at the end of the episode with the dead body?

24 What are the four ingredients of a Waldorf salad?

25 What musical instrument does Manuel play?

11

1 Which author wrote *The Sound and the Fury*, *The Wild Palms* and *As I Lay Dying*?

2 What did A E Housman's initials stand for?

3 Which E M Forster novel features the Schlegel sisters?

4 How do we better know Mrs William Heelis?

5 Which novel deals with the events of one day in Dublin in June 1904?

6 Whose first collection of short stories, entitled *In Our Time*, was published in 1925?

7 Which of Jane Austen's novels was published posthumously?

8 Who is Pip's benefactor in Dickens's *Great Expectations*?

9 In Swift's *Gulliver's Travels*, what is Gulliver's profession?

10 Which writer, archaeologist and soldier joined the RAF after the First World War and changed his name to Shaw in 1927?

11 What are the March sisters' names in Louisa M Alcott's *Little Women*?

12 Which French author's novel *Germinal* depicts life in a mining community?

13 Which English writer divided his novels into three categories: Novels of Character and Environment, Romances and Fantasies, and Novels of Ingenuity?

14 How many tales are there in Chaucer's *Canterbury Tales*?

15 Which Nobel Prize winner wrote *A History of English-speaking Peoples*?

16 Which St Louis-born novelist and poet became a British subject in 1927?

17 What is the surname of Cathy in *Wuthering Heights*?

18 What was the name of William Wordsworth's sister?

19 Whose works, *The Ballad of Reading Gaol* and *De Profundis*, were written from his experiences in prison?

20 Which thriller writer's works include *The Dark Eyes of London*, *Four Just Men* and *Sanders of the River*?

22

21 For which novel was Boris Pasternak awarded the 1958 Nobel Prize, an award he declined?

22 Which Algerian-born French author's works included *L'Etranger* and *La Peste*?

23 Which of the Brontë sisters married the Reverend A B Nicholls in 1854?

24 Whose life was the subject of James Boswell's biography, published in 1791?

25 Who wrote the Barsetshire novels?

ANSWERS TO QUIZ 10

Famous Couples

1 Jason Robards
2 Henry's brother Arthur
3 Ptolemy XII (her brother)
4 Oliver Hardy
5 Lady Godiva
6 Michael Caine
7 Gerry Goffin and Carole King
8 1840
9 Richard Wagner
10 Timothy West and Prunella Scales
11 Burt Reynolds
12 Abbott and Costello
13 1996
14 Mia Farrow
15 Peter Sellers
16 Phil Spector
17 Tony Curtis and Janet Leigh
18 Banting and Best
19 Eva Braun
20 Ike and Tina Turner
21 Hansel and Gretel
22 Barnum and Bailey
23 Simone De Beauvoir
24 Lynn Frederick
25 Blake Edwards

Screen Lovers

1 *The African Queen*
2 *The Bodyguard*
3 *Born Yesterday*
4 *Brief Encounter*
5 *Children of a Lesser God*
6 *A Countess from Hong Kong*
7 *A Farewell to Arms*
8 *Forever Young*
9 *The Ghost & Mrs Muir*
10 *LA Story*
11 *An Officer and a Gentleman*
12 *Adam's Rib*
13 *Out of Africa*
14 *Prizzi's Honor*
15 Robin Hood & Maid Marian
16 *Romancing the Stone*
17 *Roxanne*
18 *The Russia House*
19 *Shadowlands*
20 *The Way We Were*
21 *When Harry Met Sally*
22 *Working Girl*
23 *The Year of Living Dangerously*
24 *Romanoff and Juliet*
25 *Oliver's Story*

Plants

1 Daisy
2 In or around water
3 Peas
4 Borneo and Sumatra
5 They spread over the ground
6 Campanulate
7 Warm or sunny
8 Stone-breaker
9 On the trunk of a tree
10 The Venus flytrap
11 In the Alps at high altitude
12 White
13 Deadly nightshade
14 Central America's rainforest
15 Ferns
16 Its flower resembles a female bee
17 Rosemary
18 Switzerland
19 Chewing gum – peppermint or spearmint
20 An onion
21 Opium poppy
22 An annual
23 The lotus
24 An orchid
25 The dahlia

Elvis Presley

1 Tupelo, Mississippi
2 'That's All Right' and 'Blue Moon of Kentucky'
3 The Jordanaires
4 'Heartbreak Hotel'
5 Scotty Moore and Bill Black
6 *Love Me Tender*
7 'The Wonder of You' (August 1970)
8 Las Vegas
9 Jessie
10 It was Elvis's army number
11 Jerry Lieber and Mike Stoller
12 $35,000
13 Lisa Marie Presley was born
14 'Wooden Heart'
15 They are all movie characters played by Elvis
16 The Beatles
17 Kurt Russell
18 'All Shook Up' (July 1957)
19 'Crying in the Chapel'
20 Colonel Tom Parker, Elvis's manager
21 Misery
22 1961 and 1962
23 Richard Nixon
24 Carl Perkins, Jerry Lee Lewis and Johnny Cash
25 Tenor saxophone

News Events

1 1981
2 Cuba
3 Idi Amin
4 Roger Bannister ran the first sub-four-minute mile
5 Marilyn Monroe
6 1986
7 The Watergate complex, Washington, DC
8 The Treaty of Versailles
9 Robben Island, off Cape Town
10 They were Arab terrorists who stormed the Israeli building in the Olympic village near Munich
11 Benazir Bhutto
12 The assassination of President Kennedy
13 The British Government
14 The Berlin Wall
15 1959
16 Marion Barry, Mayor of Washington, DC
17 The coffin of Tutankhamun
18 1991
19 The Great Train Robbery
20 George Wallace
21 Earl Mountbatten
22 Pennsylvania
23 Black Monday, due to the stock market crash
24 The World Trade Center
25 *The Satanic Verses*

The World Cup

1 Jules Rimet
2 Uruguay
3 It was the 1,000th goal at World Cup final stages
4 He was the referee who allowed the 'hand of God' goal
5 France
6 Substitutes
7 Ten (six in 1986, four in 1990)
8 France and the USA
9 Italy v Czechoslovakia, 1934
10 The Battle of Santiago
11 Saudi Arabia
12 Lineker, Beardsley and Platt
13 Egypt, 1934
14 Alan Shearer
15 Just Fontaine of France with 13 in 1958
16 Ally MacLeod
17 Jairzinho
18 Eusebio, Portugal
19 Zaire
20 Wales
21 Italy, 1934
22 Wolfgang Weber
23 Pasadena
24 Scotland, 1974
25 Italy (1934 and 1990) and Mexico (1970 and 1986)

Fawlty Towers

1 Lord Melbury
2 Torquay
3 Back to the hotel with André's food for gourmet night
4 André
5 Terry the chef
6 Stubbs
7 Her friend's stepfather
8 Dragonfly
9 Swanage
10 Major Gowen
11 Gleneagles
12 Miss Gatsby and Miss Tibbs
13 Prunella Scales
14 A moose's head
15 An umbrella
16 Bernard Cribbins
17 Mr O'Reilly
18 Geoffrey Palmer
19 A slice of veal
20 Manuel
21 A kipper
22 Brahms
23 In the linen basket when it is collected
24 Apple, celery, walnuts, grapes
25 The guitar

Literature

1 William Faulkner
2 Alfred Edward
3 *Howard's End*
4 Beatrix Potter
5 *Ulysses* by James Joyce
6 Ernest Hemingway
7 *Persuasion*
8 Abel Magwitch
9 Surgeon
10 T E Lawrence
11 Jo, Meg, Beth and Amy
12 Emile Zola
13 Thomas Hardy
14 Twenty-three
15 Winston Churchill
16 T S Eliot
17 Earnshaw
18 Dorothy
19 Oscar Wilde
20 Edgar Wallace
21 *Dr Zhivago*
22 Albert Camus
23 Charlotte
24 Samuel Johnson
25 Anthony Trollope

THE GREATEST TRIVIA QUIZ BOOK

QUIZ 11

1 Who said, on being refused membership of an exclusive golf club, 'I'm not an actor, and I enclose my press cuttings to prove it'?

2 Of which Shakespeare role did Laurence Olivier say, 'When you've the strength for it, you're too young; when you've the age you're too old. It's a bugger, isn't it?'?

3 Who is credited with, 'A woman drove me to drink and I never even had the courtesy to thank her'?

4 Which boxer used to 'float like a butterfly, sting like a bee'?

5 Which actress is reported to have said, 'I'm as pure as the driven slush'?

6 Who, when asked what his epitaph should read, replied, 'He was an average guy who could carry a tune'?

7 At the 1963 Royal Variety Performance who said, 'Will the people in the cheaper seats clap your hands? All the rest of you, if you'll just rattle your jewellery'?

8 Which newsreader said, 'Let's face it, there are no plain women on television'?

9 Which United States president said, 'Read my lips, no new taxes'?

10 On learning that he was described as an Irishman because he was born in Dublin, who said, 'Being born in a stable does not make a man a horse'?

11 Which British Prime Minister is said to have commented to friends when first appointed, 'I have climbed to the top of the greasy pole'?

12 Which TV show featured the catchphrases 'very interesting, but stupid' and 'here come de judge'?

13 When asked what his handicap was during a game of golf, which entertainer replied, 'I'm a coloured, one-eyed Jew'?

14 Which movie mogul supposedly said, 'A verbal contract isn't worth the paper it's written on'?

15 Who said, 'Of course, America had often been discovered before Columbus, but it had always been hushed up'?

16 Who described a performance by Katharine Hepburn as running 'the entire gamut of emotions from A to B'?

17 Which American comedian said, 'Too bad all the people who know how to run the country are busy driving cabs and cutting hair'?

18 Who commented 'I used to be Snow White...but I drifted'?

19 What did politician and broadcaster Austin Mitchell describe as 'an ermine-lined dustbin, an upmarket geriatric home with a faint smell of urine'?

20 Who said 'All I need to make a comedy is a park, a policeman and a pretty girl'?

21 Which British monarch said of King Lear, 'A strange, horrible business, but I suppose good enough for Shakespeare's day'?

22 Which film director said, 'Actors should be treated like cattle'?

23 Which American comedienne said, 'Boy George is all England needs – another queen who can't dress'?

24 Who said, 'An actor's a guy who, if you ain't talking about him, ain't listening'?

25 When asked his view of Western civilisation, who replied, 'I think it would be good idea'?

1 Who played the part of The Beatles' manager in *A Hard Day's Night*?

2 In whose films was Margaret Dumont sometimes cast as a put-upon society figure?

3 Who played the scientist's assistant, Igor, in *Young Frankenstein*?

4 Which Scottish-born actor is best remembered for his exaggerated double takes in Laurel and Hardy movies?

5 Who played Gene Hackman's police partner in *The French Connection*?

6 Who was the third sailor on shore leave with Gene Kelly and Frank Sinatra in *On the Town*?

7 In which film did Fred MacMurray appear as Jack Lemmon's boss, Mr Sheldrake?

8 Which film featured singer Al Martino who, as singer Johnny Fontane, makes an appearance at a family wedding?

9 In which film did George Segal and Sandy Dennis support the leads Richard Burton and Elizabeth Taylor?

10 Who won an Academy Award for best supporting actor in Stanley Kubrick's *Spartacus*?

11 Who appeared as a blind hermit in *Young Frankenstein*?

12 Which stalwart of British horror films played Grand Moff Tarkin in *Star Wars*?

13 Which film director played a small but significant role in *Chinatown*?

14 Who provided the love interest for Jack Lemmon and Walter Matthau in *Grumpy Old Men*?

15 Which future *Baywatch* star was one of Elliott's classmates in *ET, The Extra-Terrestrial*?

16 In the 1967 film *To Sir with Love*, starring Sidney Poitier, which pop singer appeared as one

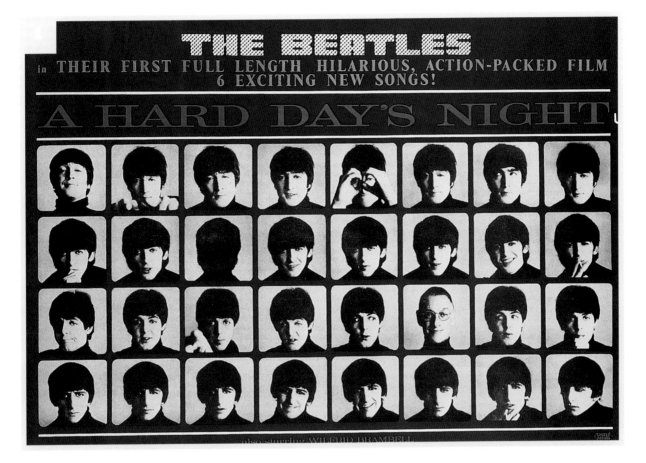

THE BEATLES
in THEIR FIRST FULL LENGTH HILARIOUS, ACTION-PACKED FILM
6 EXCITING NEW SONGS!
A HARD DAY'S NIGHT

also starring WILFRID BRAMBELL

of the pupils in addition to singing the theme song?

17 In the 1963 film version of Edgar Allan Poe's 'The Raven', which future Oscar-winning actor played Peter Lorre's son?

18 In which James Bond film did German actor Gert Frobe play the title role?

19 Which actor played supporting roles in *Jerry Maguire* and *As Good as it Gets*?

20 Which future stars of the comedy series *Taxi* played hospital patients in *One Flew Over the Cuckoo's Nest*?

21 In one of her earliest screen roles, which actress appeared with the Marx Brothers in the 1950 film *Love Happy*?

22 Which singer made his screen debut in *Catch-22* in 1970?

23 A star of Coppola's *Godfather* movies, who played the unbilled part of a businessman in *The Conversation*, under the same director?

24 What is the significance of Gregory Peck and Robert Mitchum's cameo appearances in the 1991 version of *Cape Fear*?

25 Who was nominated for a best supporting actor Oscar in *JFK*?

1 What mammal of northern Europe, Asia and North America is sometimes called a glutton?

2 What sort of animal is a fer-de-lance?

3 Which large feline of Asia is sometimes called an ounce?

4 Which rodent has given its name to a mean-spirited or bad-tempered woman?

5 What apparently inappropriate name is used for a gathering and breeding place for seals?

6 What is the main diet of the pangolin?

7 Which is the largest living carnivore?

8 The word 'ophidian' refers to what sort of animal?

9 Which large rodent's fur is known as nutria?

10 Americans call it a caribou. What is it called in Europe?

11 Dugongs and manatees belong to which family of animals?

12 The echidna, or spiny anteater, and the duck-billed platypus share a characteristic which does not apply to any other mammal. What is it?

13 Which is the largest living rodent?

14 Which two islands are the natural habitat of the orang utan?

15 Which small breed of cattle is found wild in the Tibetan plateau, north of the Himalayas?

16 Which small rodent, highly valued for its fine, silky fur, lives almost exclusively high in the Andes?

17 Which is the largest member of the cat family that is indigenous to the New World?

18 Which animal is the symbol of the World Wide Fund for Nature?

19 What is the name of the wild pig of Central and South America that has three species called collared, white-lipped and chaco?

20 Hyraxes, which grow to weigh a maximum of 5 kg and are the Conies mentioned in the Bible, have a shared ancestry with which large mammal?

21 Which is the smallest mammal in Europe?

22 Which snake is also known as a hamadryad?

23 The vicuña is a member of which family of mammals?

24 The tenrec is a small insectivore that is only found on which large island?

25 What is the largest mammal?

14

1 Which American soprano became the first singer to give a solo Proms recital in August 2000?

2 By what name is Beethoven's sixth symphony known?

3 Whose Variations on a Theme by Paganini is a standard part of the piano repertoire?

4 Which Suffolk town was the birthplace of Benjamin Britten?

5 Which composer was baptised with the forenames Johannes Chrysostamus Wolfgangus Theophilus?

6 What is meant by the musical instruction largo?

7 In a standard orchestra lineup, which musicians sit immediately to the conductor's left?

8 Who was asked in 1874 by Henrik Ibsen to write incidental music to *Peer Gynt*?

20

9 Which male vocal range is pitched between tenor and bass?

10 Whose ballet music includes *Petrushka* and *The Rite of Spring*?

11 How many keys are on a standard concert piano?

12 Which knight was until fairly recently conductor with the City of Birmingham Symphony Orchestra?

13 In 1932 Edward Elgar recorded his violin concerto. Who was the sixteen-year-old soloist?

14 Which opera overture is used as a background to post-Grand Prix champagne celebrations?

15 Which piece of music traditionally closes the last night of the Proms?

16 In 1922, which composer scored Mussorgsky's piano piece *Pictures at an Exhibition* for full orchestra?

17 Who was the first American-born principal conductor of the New York Philharmonic Orchestra?

18 What connects composers such as Haydn, Mozart, Beethoven and Schubert with the city of Vienna?

19 What was Richard Wagner composing intermittently between 1848 and 1874?

20 Which British opera festival was started in 1934?

21 What function did the composer Franz Schubert perform at Beethoven's funeral?

13

22 Which movie is synonymous with the Adagietto from Mahler's fifth symphony?

23 What do the initials FRAM stand for?

24 By what name is Antonin Dvorak's ninth symphony known?

25 Which pianist/composer/conductor was born in Berlin in 1929, took American citizenship in 1943 and became a well-known face on British TV in the 1970s?

15

5 When did the United States declare war on Germany?

6 On which peninsula did allied forces land on 25 April 1915?

7 On which islands was the naval base of Scapa Flow?

8 What type of vehicle was the Firespit II?

9 Who led the American Expeditionary Force in France?

10 What did the French begin to construct along their eastern frontier after the war?

11 What happened on the Western Front on 11 November 1918?

12 Who, or what, was 'Big Bertha'?

13 What was used in warfare for the first time in April 1915?

14 Who was Commander-in-Chief of the British Expeditionary Force?

15 How did Lord Kitchener die?

16 Who became British Prime Minister in December 1916?

17 By what name is the third Battle of Ypres commonly known?

18 To which throne was Archduke Ferdinand heir?

19 What was the longest battle of the entire war?

20 In which sea was the *Lusitania* sunk?

1 Who was recalled from retirement in 1914 to assume command of the German army in the east?

2 What was the name of Vice-Admiral Beatty's flagship at the Battle of Jutland?

3 Who was Gavrilo Princip?

4 Which battle began on 1 July 1916?

21 At which battle, in September 1916, were tanks first used?

22 What was unusual about the Russian Army's 'Battalion of Death', formed in 1917?

23 After the war, in which country did Kaiser Wilhelm II spend the rest of his life in exile?

24 In which year did military service become compulsory in Britain?

25 What type of aircraft dropped 500 bombs on England in September 1916?

25

1 Which future world heavyweight boxing champion won gold in the middleweight division at the 1976 games in Montreal?

2 Klaus Dibiasi won three consecutive platform diving medals in 1968, 1972 and 1976. Which country did he represent?

3 In which years were the Olympics held in Los Angeles?

4 At which event did swimmers Duncan Goodhew and Adrian Moorhouse win gold at Moscow and Seoul respectively?

5 Which nation won the gold medal in the Association Football event at the 1964 Tokyo games and again at Mexico City in 1968?

6 At which Olympic games did the British men's hockey team win gold?

7 How many nations were represented at the first modern games in Athens in 1896?

8 Who won Great Britain's first gold at the Sydney 2000 games?

9 At which games was the women's 400 metres hurdles first included?

10 Where and when did the games take place in the southern hemisphere for the first time?

11 At the time of writing, the men's 100 metres world record stands to Maurice Greene at 9.79 seconds. What was the winning time for the event at the 1896 games in Athens?

12 Which Ethiopian athlete won the marathon at the Rome and Tokyo games in 1960 and 1964?

13 Who lit the torch and later won a gold medal at the Sydney games?

14 Which gymnast won gold on the beam discipline at both the Montreal and Moscow games in 1976 and 1980?

15 Between 1920 and 1928, how many gold medals were won by Finnish distance runner Paavo Nurmi?

16 Which French athlete walked out of the Sydney games on the eve of the competition?

17 How did Russian Sacha Belov break American hearts at the Munich games in 1972?

18 Who was Steven Redgrave's rowing partner when he won his first two golds at Los Angeles and Seoul?

19 In which games did archery first become an Olympic sport?

20 Which Atlanta athlete broke the 200 metres world record in his home-town in 1996?

21 Which two future heavyweight boxing champions of the world won Olympic golds at that weight in 1964 and 1968 respectively?

22 Apart from being gold medallists, what did American swimmers Johnny Weissmuller and Buster Crabbe have in common?

23 Who won seven gold medals, all with world records, in the swimming pool at the 1972 Munich games?

24 What did Swedish modern pentathlon competitor Hans-Gunnar Liljenvall have the dubious distinction of being first to do at an Olympic games in Mexico City, 1968?

25 Marion Jones was expected to win five gold medals at the Sydney Olympics. How many did she actually win?

1 Which easy-listening crooner had a hit hour-long weekly variety show from 1955–1963?

2 Who topped the bill at the 1963 Royal Variety Performance?

3 Bob Horn's Bandstand began in 1952 as a local show in the Philadelphia area. By what name was it known when it went national in 1957?

4 By the time the above programme went national who was its host?

5 Which US DJ hosted the *Moondog's Rock 'n' Roll Party*?

6 Which BBC/WGBH co-production serialised the history of pop music in ten parts?

7 The Rolling Stones changed the lyrics of their 1967 single 'Let's Spend the Night Together' for *The Ed Sullivan Show*. What was the new title?

8 'The Pre-Fab Four' were the stars of a TV series that debuted in 1966. What was it called?

9 In which year did *Top of the Pops* begin?

10 Which band performed covers of songs by David Bowie, Leadbelly and the Meat Puppets during their appearance on 'Unplugged'?

11 On which TV show did the Beatles make their US TV debut?

12 How did the Sex Pistols cause outrage during an appearance on British TV in 1976?

13 Whose appearance at the 1996 Brit Awards prompted a stage invasion by Pulp's Jarvis Cocker?

14 By what name was Monkee Mickey Dolenz known in his days as a child star in *Circus Boy*?

15 Which former presenter of *The Tube* committed suicide in 2000?

16 In what way were many of Elvis Presley's early TV performances censored?

17 Who provided the voices for both Beavis and Butthead?

18 Which event dominated TV screens on 13 July 1985?

19 John Lennon became the first Beatle to appear solo when he sang his 1970 hit single on *Top of the Pops*. What was it called?

20 Which giant of easy listening once had his own show in which, amongst other things, a bear kept asking him for cookies?

21 Which show gave a backdrop of music from the charts to footage of news events beginning in the fifties?

22 Which singer, second in popularity only to Elvis Presley in the late 1950s, had his own TV show between 1957–1960?

23 Giving rise to several albums, which channel has featured artists in an 'unplugged' setting?

24 Which member of the Rat Pack had a hit TV series from 1965–74?

25 Who was prevented from singing 'Talking John Birch Society Blues' on the *Ed Sullivan Show* because the network thought it too controversial?

1 The name in Australia for methylated spirits as a drink, sometimes mixed with shoe polish, is the same as that for which cocktail consisting of gin, Cointreau, and lemon juice?

2 Excess consumption of what is thought to cause Chinese restaurant syndrome?

3 Which spirit is distilled from the agave plant?

4 What Italian term describes pasta cooked so as to be firm when eaten?

5 Which cold dessert made from milk or cream beaten with sugar, wine, and lemon juice has the same name as a spiced drink made of milk with rum, port, brandy, or wine?

6 Which capital city is associated with a large prawn that is usually used to make scampi?

7 What are the main ingredients of a Snowball cocktail?

8 What boy's name is given to a dish consisting of toast, covered with a slice of ham, poached egg, and hollandaise sauce?

9 What name is given to the balloon-shaped glass from which brandy is usually drunk?

10 Which popular, if dangerous, drink is a mixture of cider and lager?

11 What American word for rumour derives from a cask of drinking water aboard a ship?

12 What is the name for a Chinese omelette?

13 Which US slang word for inferior whiskey is also used for an aeroplane flight leaving late at night or arriving early in the morning?

14 Jambalaya, a stew made of shrimps, ham, rice, onions and other ingredients, originated in which US state?

15 Which supposed hangover cure consists of raw unbeaten egg, vinegar or Worcestershire sauce, salt, and pepper?

16 Lobster Thermidor is a dish of lobster served with which type of sauce?

17 What is the aubergine also known as?

18 'Rijsttafel' is a meal originating in which country?

19 Specifically, which spirit is the base of a mint julep?

20 What is the Japanese dish of thin fillets of raw fish called?

21 Which cocktail is made up of four parts whisky, one part vermouth, and a dash of bitters?

22 What is the Greek name for kebabs?

23 What name is given to diluted rum?

24 Which popular sweet stuff has a name derived from the Aztec for 'bitter water'?

25 What would an Australian do with an 'esky'?

17

ANSWERS TO QUIZ 11

Quotations
1 Victor Mature
2 King Lear
3 W C Fields
4 Muhammad Ali (Cassius Clay)
5 Tallulah Bankhead
6 Bing Crosby
7 John Lennon
8 Anna Ford
9 George Bush
10 The Duke of Wellington
11 Benjamin Disraeli
12 *Rowan and Martin's Laugh-In*
13 Sammy Davis, Jr
14 Sam Goldwyn
15 Oscar Wilde
16 Dorothy Parker
17 George Burns
18 Mae West
19 The House of Lords
20 Charlie Chaplin
21 Queen Victoria
22 Alfred Hitchcock
23 Joan Rivers
24 Marlon Brando
25 Mahatma Gandhi

Also Starring
1 Norman Rossington
2 The Marx Brothers
3 Marty Feldman
4 James Finlayson
5 Roy Scheider
6 Jukles Munshin
7 *The Apartment*
8 *The Godfather*
9 *Who's Afraid of Virginia Woolf?*
10 Peter Ustinov
11 Gene Hackman
12 Peter Cushing
13 Roman Polanski, *Chinatown*'s director
14 Ann-Margret
15 Erika Eleniak
16 Lulu
17 Jack Nicholson
18 *Goldfinger*
19 Cuba Gooding, Jr
20 Danny DeVito and Christopher Lloyd
21 Marilyn Monroe
22 Art Garfunkel
23 Robert Duvall
24 They were the stars of the 1962 version
25 Tommy Lee Jones

Wild Animals
1 Wolverine
2 Snake
3 Snow leopard
4 Shrew
5 Rookery
6 Ants and termites
7 Brown or grizzly bear
8 Snake
9 Coypu
10 Reindeer
11 Sirenia or sea cows
12 They lay eggs
13 Capybara
14 Borneo and Sumatra
15 Yak
16 Chinchilla
17 Jaguar
18 Giant panda
19 Peccary
20 Elephant
21 Pygmy shrew
22 King cobra
23 Llama
24 Madagascar
25 Blue whale

Classical Music
1 Jessye Norman
2 The Pastoral Symphony
3 Rachmaninoff
4 Lowestoft
5 Mozart
6 Slow, dignified in style
7 First violins
8 Edvard Grieg
9 Baritone
10 Stravinsky
11 Eighty-eight
12 Sir Simon Rattle
13 Yehudi Menuhin
14 Bizet's *Carmen*
15 'Jerusalem'
16 Ravel
17 Leonard Bernstein
18 They all died there
19 The *Ring* cycle
20 Glyndebourne
21 He was a pallbearer
22 *Death in Venice*
23 Fellow of the Royal Academy of Music
24 *From the New World*
25 André Previn

World War I
1 Field Marshal von Hindenburg
2 The Lion
3 He assassinated Archduke Franz Ferdinand
4 The Battle of the Somme
5 April 1917
6 Gallipoli
7 The Orkneys
8 A British tank
9 General John J Pershing
10 The Maginot Line
11 Hostilities ceased
12 A 42 cm German field gun
13 Poison gas
14 Sir Douglas Haig
15 Aboard the *Hampshire*, which struck a mine
16 Lloyd George
17 Passchendale
18 Austro-Hungarian
19 Verdun, February to December 1916
20 The Irish Sea
21 The Somme
22 It was a battalion of women
23 Holland
24 1916
25 Zeppelins

The Olympics
1 Michael Spinks, USA
2 Italy
3 1932 and 1984
4 100 metres breaststroke
5 Hungary
6 Seoul, 1988
7 Fourteen
8 Jason Queally, 1 km cycling time trial
9 Los Angeles, 1984
10 Melbourne, 1956
11 12 seconds
12 Abebe Bikila
13 Cathy Freeman
14 Nadia Comaneci, Romania
15 Nine
16 Marie-José Perec
17 He scored the last-second winning basket to inflict the first ever defeat of the USA Olympic basketball team
18 Andrew Holmes
19 Munich, 1972
20 Michael Johnson
21 Joe Frazier and George Foreman
22 They both went on to movie careers
23 Mark Spitz
24 Fail a drugs test
25 Three

Music Shows
1 Perry Como
2 The Beatles
3 *American Bandstand*
4 Dick Clark
5 Alan Freed
6 *Dancing in the Street*
7 'Let's spend *some time* together'
8 *The Monkees*
9 1964
10 Nirvana
11 *The Ed Sullivan Show*
12 By swearing
13 Michael Jackson
14 Mickey Braddock
15 Paula Yates
16 He was shown only from the waist up
17 Mike Judge
18 Live Aid
19 'Instant Karma!'
20 Andy Williams
21 The Banana Splits
22 Pat Boone
23 MTV
24 Dean Martin
25 Bob Dylan

Food & Drink
1 White Lady
2 Monosodium glutamate
3 Tequila
4 Al dente
5 Syllabub
6 Dublin (Bay prawns)
7 Advocaat and lemonade
8 Benedict (Eggs Benedict)
9 Snifter
10 Snakebite
11 Scuttlebutt
12 Foo yong
13 Redeye
14 Louisiana
15 Prairie oyster
16 Cheese sauce
17 Egg plant
18 Indonesia
19 Bourbon whiskey
20 Sashimi
21 Manhattan
22 Souvlaki
23 Grog
24 Chocolate
25 Keep food/drink cold

THE GREATEST TRIVIA QUIZ BOOK

QUIZ 12

1 Who became Prime Minister of Israel in 1969?

2 With which political movement is the name Emmeline Pankhurst associated?

3 Who learnt English at an abbey in Dublin in order to teach Indian and Anglo-Saxon girls in Calcutta, where she worked prior to taking her vows as a nun in 1931?

4 Which Burmese politician, winner of the 1991 Nobel Peace Prize, was under house arrest from 1988 to 1995?

5 Which female scientist received the Nobel Prize for Chemistry in 1911?

6 Of whom did Charlotte Brontë say, 'Stronger than a man, simpler than a child, her nature stood alone'?

7 Which Polish chemist discovered radium and polonium?

8 What was Hillary Clinton's maiden name?

9 Edith Head's name appeared many times on movie credits. What was her contribution?

10 What was Mrs Beeton's Christian name?

11 Which woman was one of the founders of United Artists in 1919?

12 Soprano Maria Callas was born Maria Kalogeropoulas in 1923 in which city?

13 Who wrote *Sex and the Single Girl* in 1962 and later revitalised *Cosmopolitan* magazine?

14 By what title do we now know the woman born Margaret Hilda Roberts in 1926?

15 Which event of 1936 was documented by German filmmaker Leni Riefenstahl?

16 By what nickname was American all-round sports star of the 30s, 40s and 50s Mildred Didrikson better known?

17 Whose diary was written as a series of letters to an imaginary friend called Kitty?

18 Who succeeded Lal Shastri as India's Prime Minister in 1966?

19 Who was canonised in 1920, 489 years after her death?

20 By what name is Princess Sophia of Anhalt-Zerbst better remembered?

21 What did Russian Valentina Tereshkova become the first woman to do in 1963?

22 Which American actress is married to Baron Haden-Guest?

23 Of which country was Benazir Bhutto prime minister between 1988–90 and 1993–96?

24 Which writer, lecturer, broadcaster and champion of feminism was born in Melbourne in 1939?

25 Who, at the age of eighty-seven, became the first woman to receive the Order of Merit in 1907?

12

4 In 1951 Howard Hawks produced *The Thing*. Who directed the 1982 remake, starring Kurt Russell?

5 Which 1922 German vampire film starred the genuinely scary-looking Max Schreck in the title role?

6 Who played Jack Nicholson's wife in *The Shining*?

7 Who directed the 1968 film *Rosemary's Baby*?

8 Which of Courteney Cox's co-stars from the *Scream* films is now her husband?

9 Who played the monster in the 1931 film *Frankenstein*?

10 What particular gimmick was used in the 1958 film *House of Wax*?

11 Who played the title role in the 1960 Hammer production *The Curse of the Werewolf*?

12 Which 1945 Ealing film is a sequence of supernatural stories told by a group of people in a country house?

13 Which horror film star was portrayed in an Oscar-winning performance by Martin Landau in Tim Burton's 1994 film about cult filmmaker Ed Wood?

14 Which mother and daughter both appeared in John Carpenter's *The Fog*?

15 Which 1976 film is about a persecuted schoolgirl with psychokinetic powers?

16 Which actor of the silent era was known as 'The Man of a Thousand Faces'?

1 In which series of films from 1984 onwards did Robert Englund star as Freddy Krueger?

2 Which film first featured a character later called Pinhead?

3 Who played the title role in *The Abominable Dr Phibes*?

17 What was the contribution of actress Mercedes McCambridge to Linda Blair's performance in *The Exorcist*?

18 Apart from Anthony Perkins, which other performer from *Psycho* also appeared in *Psycho II* twenty-three years later?

19 What is the title of the 1992 Belgian film about a film crew following the exploits of a serial killer?

20 Which series of films features a habitual killer called Michael Myers?

21 What is the significance of the 1976 film *To the Devil . . . A Daughter*?

22 Which director's films include *Shivers*, *Videodrome* and *The Fly*?

23 What is the name of the summer camp in the *Friday the Thirteenth* movies?

24 Who played the title role in the 1965 British film *The Nanny*?

25 Played subsequently by Sarah Michelle Gellar on TV, which eponymous character was played in a movie by Kristy Swanson?

17

8

1 In which country is Europe's highest mountain, Mt Elbrus?

2 Which metallic element has the symbol Eu?

3 In which century was the Canal du Midi opened, connecting the Atlantic Ocean to the Mediterranean Sea?

4 What nationality was the chemist Alfred Nobel?

5 If you drove in a straight line from Moscow to Madrid how many countries would you drive in altogether?

6 Which mountain range lies in the north of Spain, west of the Pyrenees?

7 Created by German scientists in 1876, what was the first artificial flavouring?

8 Which European country generates the highest proportion of its electricity by hydroelectric power stations?

9 Where is the Glenveagh National Park?

10 Between which two countries would you find Lake Olirid?

11 In 1904 Danish biologist Johannes Schmidt discovered the Sargasso Sea in the North Atlantic to be the breeding ground of which fish?

12 Which European country is the world's largest producer of cork?

13 What forms the natural border between Europe and Asia?

14 What nationality was Christian Schonbein, who discovered ozone in 1840?

15 Which two countries have coastlines on the Bay of Biscay?

16 Into where does the Volga, Europe's longest river, flow?

17 Which country is the world's leading exporter of salmon?

18 Artificial PKN fertilisers were introduced in Britain in 1926. What are the constituent parts?

19 What is the second official language spoken in Germany?

20 What separates Spain from Morocco?

21 Lake Ladoga is the largest lake in which country?

22 In which country are the Apennine Mountains?

23 Which country has borders with France, Germany, Austria, Lichtenstein and Italy?

24 Between which two countries would you find the Gulf of Bothnia?

25 What is common to the Republic of Ireland, Northern Ireland, Scotland, Wales, Monaco, Denmark and Portugal?

1 Who is the youngest member of Boyzone?

2 Whose debut hit 'No No No' featured ex-Fugee Wyclef Jean?

3 Which teen boy band did Johnny Wright manage before Backstreet Boys?

4 At which summer event in 2000 did Christina Aguilera make her live UK debut?

5 What was Robbie Williams' first UK number 1?

6 How were New Kids on the Block billed after a three-year absence from the charts with their 1994 efforts 'Dirty Dawg' and 'Never Let You Go'?

7 Which American vocal group scored their first UK hit in 1995 with 'We've Got It Goin' On'?

8 Robbie Williams has had by far the most success of the former members of Take That. Gary Barlow and Mark Owen have enjoyed some measure of success, but what are the names of the other two?

9 With which boy band did Mariah Carey cover the Phil Collins hit 'Against All Odds'?

10 Boyzone's first UK hit was 'Love Me for a Reason' in 1994. In which year did the Osmonds take the song to number one in Britain?

11 Released in May 1999, what was Geri Halliwell's first solo single?

12 Which song gave Hanson a transatlantic number 1 in 1997?

13 Which girl group had hits with 'Give It Up, Turn It Loose', 'Whatta Man' and 'Don't Let Go (Love)'?

14 Which American R&B/pop quintet released the album *No Strings Attached* in 2000?

15 Which Swedish four-piece recorded the best-selling debut album of all time?

16 The ever-changing Latin teen group Menudo saw one of their old boys enjoy worldwide success in 1999. Who is he?

17 With which teen band did Bobby Brown sing before going solo?

18 What was the first Spice Girls single not to top the UK charts?

19 Which artist topped the US Billboard singles chart, the Latino singles and Latino album chart all in the same week in October 2000?

20 Which band sang Britney Spears' 'Baby One More Time' at Glastonbury 2000?

21 Which group was put together for a TV programme based in Miami?

22 With whom did Boyz II Men record the single 'One Sweet Day' in 1995?

23 What world record does *Crazysexycool* by TLC hold?

24 Which film featured R. Kelly's 'I Believe I Can Fly'?

25 All Saints' hit 'Pure Shores' was taken from the soundtrack of which film?

10

1 Who was the first Catholic president of the United States?

2 In 1960 Penguin books announced that they would be publishing which controversial novel?

3 Which government post was held by John Profumo at the time of the affair involving Christine Keeler?

4 Who was shot dead in Dallas on 24 November 1963?

5 With which band did The Jimi Hendrix Experience's record producer/manager Chas Chandler make his name?

6 Who moved into his 'Factory' on New York's East 47th Street in 1963?

7 In which year was the Berlin Wall constructed?

8 Whose death in 1965 prompted President Johnson to order that all American flags the world over be flown at half-mast, a mark of respect never before accorded to a foreigner?

9 Which revolutionary icon was killed on 9 October 1967?

10 Who directed Terence Stamp in his first starring role in the film *Billy Budd* in 1962?

11 To what did the chant 'Hell, no! We won't go!' refer?

12 What happened at Max Yasgur's dairy farm in New York state during 15–17 August 1969?

13 What did Frenchman André Turcat do on 2 March 1969?

14 What happened to the Apollo I spacecraft on 27 January 1967?

15 Which founder of the Organisation for Afro-American Unity was murdered in Harlem on 21 February 1965?

16 When was the death penalty finally abolished in the UK?

17 In 1969 Richard Cawston made a documentary film for the BBC about which famous family?

18 Where did Harold Macmillan make his famous 'Winds of Change' speech in 1969?

19 In which year did the oil tanker Torrey Canyon come aground near Land's End, causing a major environmental disaster?

20 Who, in 1963, became the first film star to earn a million dollars for a single film?

21 What connects Richard Nixon, Lyndon B Johnson, Hubert Humphrey and Spiro Agnew?

22 In which year did a Soviet cosmonaut make the first spacewalk?

23 In December 1967, fifty-three-year-old Louis Washkansky became the first person to undergo what?

24 How did UN Secretary-General Dag Hammarskjoeld die in September 1961?

25 In which month of which year was the six-day war between the Arabs and the Israelis?

6

1 What are the four majors in men's golf?

2 Tiger Woods and Phil Mickelson are two of only three players to win twelve titles while in their twenties. Who is the third?

3 In which year did Nick Faldo come from six shots behind Greg Norman on the last day to win his third US Masters title?

4 Who captained America to Ryder Cup victory in 1999?

5 Who achieved the first televised hole in one on British TV?

6 The golfer pictured left won the Open in 1961 and 1962. Who is he?

7 Which women's tournament is played annually at Rancho Mirage, California?

8 At which course would you (hopefully) find the Road Hole?

9 What nationality is golfer Vijay Singh?

10 What is the term for a hole played in three shots below par?

11 The Open is always played on a links course. What is the main characteristic of a links?

12 Which British player won the women's US Open in 1987?

13 Whose real first name is Eldrick?

14 In what type of event do two players play against each another as opposed to playing against the entire field?

15 Which British-based tournament is currently sponsored by Weetabix?

16 When the flight of a golf ball curves slightly right to left it is called 'draw'. What is a slight curve of flight from left to right called?

17 Which golfer won the Open in 1987, 1990 and 1992?

18 Which is the only one of the majors to be staged at the same course every year?

19 How many majors have been won by Jack Nicklaus?

20 Ben Hogan was the last man before Tiger Woods to do what?

21 What is the name of the trophy awarded to the winner of the Open?

22 What name is given to the area containing the 11th, 12th and 13th holes at the Augusta National championship course?

23 What name is given to a score, decided on by the tournament organisers, above which a player may not progress into the next round?

24 What is the women's equivalent of the Ryder Cup?

25 What separates the Muirfield course from the Muirfield Village course?

20

1 Which supersoap had the working title "Oil"?

2 Which US soap was mentioned in *Friends*, in connection with Joey's acting career?

3 Which sitcom satirized daytime soaps and featured the catchphrase "Confused? You will be!"

4 What was America's first prime-time TV soap opera?

5 What was the spin-off series from *Dallas*?

6 Which supersoap featured actors who had previously starred in *I Dream of Jeannie* and *The Man from Atlantis*?

7 Which American soap features various members of the Foster family?

8 What is the name of the setting for Australian soap *Home and Away*?

9 Which soap, a spin-off from *Dynasty*, starred Charlton Heston, Katharine Ross, and Barbara Stanwyck?

10 Which American soap starred Jane Wyman and was set in California's wine region?

11 Who wrote the script for an unmade movie in 1974 that later became the TV series *ER*?

12 What part did John Forsythe, *Dynasty*'s Blake Carrington, play in the hit TV series *Charlie's Angels*?

13 What was Dr Kildare's Christian name?

14 What is the world's longest-running soap opera?

15 Who did Aaron Spelling cast as Donna Martin in *Beverly Hills 90210*?

16 Which soap was set in Wentworth Detention Centre, Melbourne?

17 Which TV show saw the first appearance of the character Lou Grant?

18 In which US state was *Knot's Landing* set?

19 Why are soap operas so called?

20 Complete the name of this US soap: *Sunset *****?

21 Which star of a famous soap went on to appear in several mini-series, including *Shogun*?

22 The UK's first indigenous medical soap was also the country's first twice-weekly serial. What was it called?

23 How many Emmys did *ER* win in its first year?

24 Name two of the four Dallas spin-offs.

25 In a 1983 episode of which soap did former US president Gerald Ford and former Secretary of State Henry Kissinger appear at a ball?

1 What is the rubber or metal tip of a walking stick or umbrella called?

2 What originally came in an 8" size, then $5^{1/4}$", and is presently $3^{1/2}$"?

3 What name is given to the lens or combination of lenses forming the image in a camera or projector?

4 From which material is a snooker cue tip made?

5 On what can music or data be recorded as a series of metallic pits enclosed in PVC to be read by an optical laser?

6 What aid to vision was invented by Benjamin Franklin?

7 Which saying originates from the name given to a small metallic knob acting as the sight of a firearm?

8 What word of Italian origin describes the lower part of an interior wall that is decorated differently from the upper part?

9 What is a tabor?

10 Which small handtool shares its name with a cocktail consisting of half gin or vodka and half lime juice?

11 What collective noun for finches is also a small object worn or kept for magical powers of protection?

12 The name of which popular spirit is also a type of trap?

13 What does the Australian term 'to pass in one's marble' mean?

14 What is a sneck?

15 What is the name of the small wooden or plastic peg used in golf?

16 What is the name of a small rod originally designed to get rid of carbon dioxide from fizzy drinks?

17 Which part of a drill or lathe can be a 'three jaw' or 'four jaw'?

18 Which rodent is also a computer control device?

19 What is made in a cafetière?

20 On what would you find an aglet?

21 What is a 'waiter's friend'?

22 Which common object used in an indoor game is made of crystallite?

23 Which household appliance is driven by a magnetron?

24 A 'bertha' could be which part of an item of clothing?

25 What are the metal strips on the neck of a guitar called?

ANSWERS TO QUIZ 12

Famous Women
1 Golda Meir
2 The campaign for universal suffrage
3 Agnes Bojaxhiu, later Mother Teresa
4 Aung San Suu Kyi
5 Marie Curie
6 Her sister Emily
7 Marie Curie
8 Rodham
9 Costume design
10 Isabella
11 Mary Pickford
12 New York
13 Helen Gurley Brown
14 Baroness Thatcher
15 The Berlin Olympics
16 Babe
17 Anne Frank
18 Indira Gandhi
19 Joan of Arc
20 Catherine the Great
21 Travel in space
22 Jamie Lee Curtis
23 Pakistan
24 Germaine Greer
25 Florence Nightingale

Horror Films
1 The *Nightmare on Elm Street* series
2 *Hellraiser*
3 Vincent Price
4 John Carpenter
5 *Nosferatu*
6 Shelley Duvall
7 Roman Polanski
8 David Arquette
9 Boris Karloff
10 It was made in 3-D
11 Oliver Reed
12 *Dead of Night*
13 Bela Lugosi
14 Janet Leigh and Jamie Lee Curtis
15 *Carrie*
16 Lon Chaney
17 She provided the Devil's voice
18 Vera Miles
19 *Man Bites Dog*
20 The *Halloween* series
21 It was the last horror film made by Hammer
22 David Cronenberg
23 Camp Crystal Lake
24 Bette Davis
25 Buffy the Vampire Slayer

Europe
1 The Russian Federation
2 Europium
3 Seventeenth (1681)
4 Swedish
5 Eight (Russian Federation, Belarus, Poland, Czech Republic, Germany, Switzerland, France and Spain)
6 The Cantabrian Mountains
7 Vanilla essence
8 Norway
9 County Donegal, Republic of Ireland
10 Albania and Macedonia
11 European eel
12 Portugal
13 The Ural Mountains
14 German
15 France and Spain
16 The Caspian Sea
17 Norway
18 Phosphorus, potash and nitrogen
19 Turkish
20 The Strait of Gibraltar
21 The Russian Federation
22 Italy
23 Switzerland
24 Sweden and Finland
25 They all have a coastline and a land border with only one other country

Teen Pop
1 Ronan Keating
2 Destiny's Child
3 New Kids On The Block
4 London's Party in the Park
5 'Millennium'
6 NKOTB
7 Backstreet Boys
8 Howard Donald and Jason Orange
9 Westlife
10 1974
11 'Look at Me'
12 'Mmmbop'
13 En Vogue
14 N'Sync
15 Ace of Base
16 Ricky Martin
17 New Edition
18 'Stop'
19 Christina Aguilera
20 Travis
21 S Club 7
22 Mariah Carey
23 Biggest-selling US album ever by an all-female act
24 *Space Jam*
25 *The Beach*

The 1960s
1 John F Kennedy
2 *Lady Chatterley's Lover*
3 Secretary of State for War
4 Lee Harvey Oswald
5 The Animals
6 Andy Warhol
7 1961
8 Winston Churchill
9 Che Guevara
10 Peter Ustinov
11 The war in Vietnam
12 The Woodstock festival
13 He flew Concorde on her maiden flight
14 It caught fire on the launch pad, killing all three crew
15 Malcolm X
16 1969
17 The royal family
18 Cape Town, South Africa
19 1967
20 Elizabeth Taylor in *Cleopatra*
21 They were the four US vice presidents during the 1960s
22 1965
23 A heart transplant operation
24 In an air crash
25 June 1967

Golf
1 US Masters, US Open, The Open and the US PGA
2 David Duval
3 1996
4 Ben Crenshaw
5 Tony Jacklin
6 Arnold Palmer
7 The Nabisco Dinah Shore
8 The Old Course, St Andrews
9 Fijian
10 An albatross
11 It is by the sea
12 Laura Davies
13 Tiger Woods
14 Match play
15 The Women's British Open
16 Fade
17 Nick Faldo
18 US Masters, Augusta
19 18 (6 Masters, 4 US Open, 3 Open, 5 US PGA)
20 He won three of the four majors in one year
21 The claret jug
22 Amen Corner
23 The cut
24 The Solheim Cup
25 Over 4,000 miles (Muirfield is in Scotland, Muirfield Village in Columbus, Ohio)

Soap Operas
1 *Dynasty*
2 *Days of Our Lives*
3 *Soap*
4 *Peyton Place*
5 *Knots Landing*
6 *Dallas*
7 *The Bold and the Beautiful*
8 Summer Bay
9 *The Colbys*
10 *Falcon Crest*
11 Michael Crichton
12 He was the voice of Charlie
13 James
14 *Coronation Street*
15 His daughter Tori
16 *Prisoner: Cell Block H*
17 *The Mary Tyler Moore Show*
18 California
19 Because soap manufacturers used to sponsor them
20 *Beach*
21 Richard Chamberlain
22 *Emergency Ward 10*
23 Eight
24 *Knot's Landing, Flamingo Road, Falcon Crest, King's Crossing*
25 *Dynasty*

Objects
1 A ferrule
2 Floppy disc
3 Objective or object glass
4 The ankle
5 A compact disc
6 Bifocal lens
7 To draw a bead
8 Dado
9 A small drum
10 A gimlet
11 A charm
12 Gin
13 To die
14 A catch or latch
15 A tee
16 A swizzle stick
17 A chuck
18 A mouse
19 Coffee
20 A shoelace
21 Combined knife, corkscrew and bottle-opener
22 Vulcanized rubber
23 A microwave oven
24 A collar
25 Frets

THE GREATEST TRIVIA
QUIZ BOOK

QUIZ 13

1 What is the name given to the last man in a team to compete or, in a tug-of-war team, the man furthest from the opposition?

2 Which team was founded by one Abe Saperstein and is not unfamiliar with 'Sweet Georgia Brown'?

3 In Australia, in which sort of team might you find a 'belt man'?

4 Still down under, what was the job of a 'bullocky'?

5 By what name was the US basketball team that won the 1992 and 1996 Olympic finals known?

6 What name is given to the word game in which one team says a rhyme or rhyming line for a word or line given by the other team?

7 Who won the first Superbowl, in 1967?

8 Can you name one of the two French words which are often used to describe a motor racing team?

9 Traditionally, which order is given to a team of dogs to make them start or go faster?

10 By what name were the group of young actors including Sean Penn, Emilio Estevez and Demi Moore known?

23

11 What is the name of the NFL team based in the city of Seattle?

12 Teams from which country wear the silver fern?

13 In American football what name is given to the predetermined sets of players used at kickoffs and when an attempt is made at a field goal?

14 Which member of the Magnificent Seven was also a Man from U.N.C.L.E.?

15 What is a 'dog train'?

16 How many players are there in a netball team?

17 Which word is often used for a member of a team who is a burden to the rest of the team?

18 Which term is used for a team that has not qualified for a competition but is allowed to take part, at the organisers' discretion?

19 Which country won the first football World Cup?

20 Which city's American football team is called the Bears?

21 What is the name given to the annual international lawn tennis championship for men's teams?

22 How many substitutes are allowed in a basketball team?

23 What collective name was given to Frank Sinatra, Peter Lawford, Joey Bishop, Dean Martin and Sammy Davis, Jr?

24 Forever linked with The Beatles, Shea Stadium is home to which baseball team?

25 Which 1993 movie was based on the true story of the Jamaican bobsleigh team which amused the world at the 1988 Olympics?

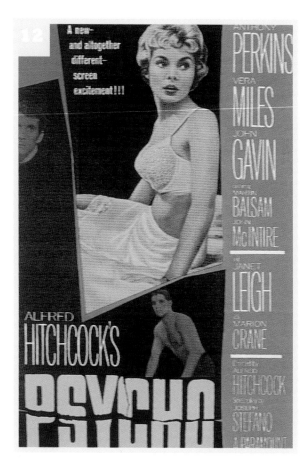

1 How does Hitchcock appear in *Strangers on a Train*?

2 What was the first film Hitchcock directed in America?

3 In which psychological thriller did Sean Connery star alongside Tippi Hedren?

4 In which film is James Stewart convinced that a murder has been committed by Raymond Burr?

5 Who wrote the novel on which Hitchcock's 1936 film *The Secret Agent* is based?

6 Who rejected the lead role in the 1940 film *Foreign Correspondent* before it was given to Joel McCrea?

7 Which artist was behind Gregory Peck's dream sequence in *Spellbound*?

8 Which film was Hitchcock's first voluntary experiment with a single setting?

9 What does Cary Grant discover in some wine bottles in *Notorious*?

10 Who plays the evil Uncle Charlie in *Shadow of a Doubt*?

11 In which film does Hitchcock appear walking out of a pet shop with some dogs?

12 How much money does Janet Leigh steal from her employer before checking in at the Bates Motel?

13 Leslie Banks played the male lead in Hitchcock's original version of *The Man who Knew Too Much* in 1934. Who was the male lead in the 1956 version?

14 In which film do John Laurie and Peggy Ashcroft appear as a farmer and his wife?

15 Hume Cronyn appears in the 1943 film *Lifeboat*, but what was his contribution to the 1948 film *Rope*?

16 Which film ends with a gripping (literally) scene at the top of the Statue of Liberty?

17 Which actor stars in *Rope* and *Strangers on a Train*?

18 From which Shakespeare play is the title *North by Northwest* indirectly taken?

19 In which year did Hitchcock receive the Irving Thalberg Award from the Academy of Motion Picture Arts and Sciences?

20 What is significant about the 1925 film *The Pleasure Garden*?

21 In which Hitchcock film does Doris Day sing the Oscar-winning song 'What Will Be, Will Be'?

22 Who made her screen debut in the 1956 film *The Trouble with Harry*?

23 In which 1955 film does Cary Grant star with Grace Kelly?

24 What was the first of Grace Kelly's three films for Hitchcock?

25 Who played the part of Father Michael Logan in the 1952 film *I Confess*?

19

1 Which African country is the largest in area?

2 In which country are the Central Kalahari Game Reserve and the Gemsbok National Park?

3 Which river separates Zimbabwe from South Africa?

4 How many African countries do not have a coastline?

5 Which snake has distinctive orange and black bands the length of its body?

6 From which lake does the White Nile begin its course?

7 What is the more common name of the large, odd-looking bird variously called boatbill or whalebill?

8 With more than 11.5 million inhabitants, which African city has the greatest population?

9 Adopted as a national emblem, what is the only gazelle found in the southern drylands?

10 What makes up roughly one-fifth of the continent's surface area?

11 Would you see a zebra in western Africa?

12 Which stretch of water lies to the north of Somalia, on the horn of Africa?

13 Zanzibar lies off the coast of which country?

14 What natural feature lies to the south and east of the Ethiopian plateau, and extends down through Kenya and Tanzania?

15 What is significant about the Banc D'Arguin National Park in Mauritania in the northwest?

16 How many types of seal are resident to African shores?

17 Which types of bird gather in millions on the shallow soda lakes of East Africa?

18 At 2,900 miles, what is Africa's second-longest river, seventh longest in the world?

19 By what name do we more commonly know *Panthera leo*?

20 In Africa, which breed of crocodile thrives over the widest area: the dwarf, the African slender-snouted or the Nile?

21 What type of animal has species named Grant's and Thompson's?

22 How many African countries lie on the equator?

23 Which country protrudes inland from the Atlantic coast, and is otherwise completely surrounded by Senegal?

24 In which country are the Maasai-Mara National Reserve and the Serengeti National Park?

25 In December 1497 Vasco da Gama made the first documented evidence of which type of animal?

1 For what do the letters SYSLJFM stand in Joe Tex's 'The Letter Song'?

2 Which British female singer recorded an album in Memphis with Jerry Wexler producing?

3 Who is regarded as 'The Godfather of Soul'?

4 Which singer was the father of Linda Womack?

5 By what collective name were Steve Cropper, Donald 'Duck' Dunn and Al Jackson known?

6 Lou Rawls, Sam and Dave, Wilson Pickett, Otis Redding: who is next in line and why?

7 Which soul artist died at the very end of 1999, having been confined to a wheelchair since 1990 after a stage lighting rig fell on him?

8 What instrument was played by King Curtis?

9 Who had a hit in 1966 with 'Tell It Like It Is'?

10 Who is known as 'Lady Soul'?

11 What colour onions were the subject of a Booker T and the MGs tune?

12 Which area of New York City was immortalised in a dance song by Bob and Earl?

13 Who was lead singer with Harold Melvin and the Bluenotes on such songs as 'The Love I Lost' and 'If You Don't Know Me By Now'?

14 Whose magnificent bald head featured on the cover of his *Hot Buttered Soul* album?

15 Which singer is known as 'The Wicked'?

16 Maurice White was a session drummer playing on Chess hits such as 'Rescue Me' by Fontella Bass. Which soul/funk band did he go on to form in the 1970s?

17 How do we better know Messrs Moore and Prater?

18 What is the rest of this James Brown song title: 'Say it Loud...'?

19 Which family group had hits on the Stax label with 'Respect Yourself' and 'I'll Take You There'?

20 In which comedy film does Aretha Franklin, cast as a proprietress of a soul food joint, sing her 1968 hit 'Think'?

21 Which songwriters formed Philadelphia International Records?

22 Which soul artist was the surprise hit of the otherwise flowery 1967 Monterey pop festival?

23 Who picked up an Academy Award in 1971 for best film song?

24 Who had a heart attack on stage in 1975 and remained in a coma until his death in 1984?

25 When Aretha Franklin got married in 1978, which Stevie Wonder song did the Four Tops sing as she walked down the aisle?

25

1 In which decade did people in Britain over the age of 65 first receive state pensions?

2 Who said in 1960 that politicians 'are the same all over. They promise to build a bridge even when there is no water'?

3 What was signed by the Soviet Union, Poland, Hungary, Czechoslovakia, Romania, Bulgaria, Albania and East Germany in 1955?

4 Who won the Fermanagh and South Tyrone by-election from his prison cell in April 1981?

5 Of which organisation was Yuri Andropov leader before becoming Soviet president in 1982?

6 What was the principal reason for the British Government's introduction of 'daylight saving time' in 1916?

7 Which country issued a Unilateral Declaration of Independence from Britain, on Remembrance Day 1965?

8 Which country's parliament was opened by King George V in 1921?

9 In 1971, which British Secretary of State for Education refused to allow local councils to supply free milk to schoolchildren?

10 A group from which political party organised a 'Stop Kennedy' campaign during the 1960 presidential election campaign?

11 By what name was Mao Tse-tung's purge on liberal dissidents in China between 1966–69 known?

12 In which year was the Israeli prime minister Yitzhak Rabin assassinated?

13 In which European city was the cease-fire agreement to end the war in Vietnam signed?

14 Who was ousted from power by hard-line Soviet communists in 1991?

15 What was the name given to the demonstration in Washington, DC led by the Nation of Islam's leader, Louis Farrakhan, in 1995?

16 Where did Nelson Mandela spend the majority of his time as a political prisoner?

17 Who is pictured right?

18 Which businessman was behind the United Empire Party in Britain in the 1930s?

19 Which Irish party's name translates as 'Soldiers of Destiny'?

20 What do the initials of the ZANU party stand for?

21 Which Democratic Party candidate ran against George Bush in the 1988 presidential election campaign?

22 Who was Prime Minister when the British Government imposed direct rule on Northern Ireland in 1972?

23 Who shared the Nobel Peace Prize in 1993?

24 Who led the Khmer Rouge from 1962–1985?

25 When were women first admitted to the House of Lords?

1 In which round did the last bare-knuckle heavyweight title fight end in 1889?

2 Which boxer was the first to have oxygen administered to him at a fight in 1903?

3 What distinction did referee Stan Christodoulou achieve in 1991?

4 Who was on the canvas for the infamous 'long count' in 1927?

5 At what age did Puerto Rican Wilfred Benitez win the world junior middleweight title in 1976?

6 By what name is John Sholto Douglas better remembered?

7 Which world middleweight champion added the epithet 'Marvelous' to his name?

8 Which British boxer is known as the Fleetwood Assassin?

9 Who was the only fighter to defeat Sugar Ray Leonard in his professional career?

10 Whose professional career started and ended with fights against Tunney Hunsaker and Trevor Berbick respectively?

11 Who did Rocky Marciano defeat to become world heavyweight champion in 1952?

12 Which British middleweight won the world title from Sugar Ray Robinson in July 1951, but lost the rematch two months later?

13 Which famous fight is the subject of the movie *When We Were Kings*?

14 Which middleweight champion was portrayed by Robert De Niro in the film *Raging Bull*?

15 What was so distinctive about the Corbett v Fitzsimmons heavyweight title fight in 1897?

16 Who was the first heavyweight to regain the world title?

17 Which British fighter's entrance into the ring prompted commentator Reg Gutteridge to announce, 'The ego has landed'?

18 Which Mexican fighter won 97 of his 100 professional fights between 1980 and 1996?

19 Which fighter was known as 'The Hitman'?

20 At what age did Naseem Hamed become WBO world featherweight champion?

21 What distinction is held by Eva Shain of New Jersey?

22 At which weight did Audley Harrison win Olympic gold in Sydney?

23 Who beat Trevor Berbick in 1986 to win his first heavyweight title, the WBC?

24 Which Scottish boxer did Alexis Arguello beat to win the world lightweight title in 1980?

25 What achievement is shared by Hungarian Laszlo Papp and Cuban Teofilio Stevenson?

1 Who is Shaggy's canine companion?

2 Which cartoon series is set in Arlen, Texas?

3 What is the name of Barney and Betty Rubble's son in *The Flintstones*?

4 With which character do you associate Elmer Fudd and Yosemite Sam?

5 Which series features a family with an evil baby and a talking dog?

6 In which cartoon series was Harry Boyle the central character?

7 Who provided the voices for Warner Bros cartoon characters such as Bugs Bunny, Daffy Duck and many others?

8 How many digits do the Simpsons have on each hand?

9 Which member of the Peanuts gang plays the piano?

10 From which country does Asterix originate?

11 Which glamorous character drove the Compact Pussycat in the Wacky Races?

12 Who is the puddy tat that Tweety Pie tawt he taw?

13 Which park is the home of Yogi Bear?

14 On which TV character was Top Cat based?

15 Jason Alexander is the voice of Duckman. On which sitcom was he a regular cast member?

16 What is the name of the vacuum cleaner in *Teletubbies*?

17 What is the connection between the Teenage Mutant Hero Turtles and the ceiling of the Sistine Chapel?

18 Who is Top Cat's long-suffering uniformed adversary?

19 Whose co-stars were a muskrat and a mole?

20 What is the Flintstones' home-town?

21 Who created Beavis and Butthead?

22 Which cartoon pop group had a UK number one hit in 1969?

23 What was the cat's name in Pixie and Dixie?

24 Which series features a character who is always getting killed?

25 Which producer is best known for his association with Tom and Jerry?

1 What type of product is made by the company founded in Chicago in 1901 by Henry Williamson Gossard?

2 Scotsman John Lawson Johnston produced a 'fluid extract of beef' mixed with caramel, salt and spices in the 1870s. What is it called?

3 Who started a company called the General Seafoods Corporation in Massachusetts in 1924 and whose name is synonymous with frozen food?

4 Which drink was first sold at Jacob's Pharmacy in Atlanta, Georgia in 1886?

5 In which year did the first Dr Martens boots come off the UK production line?

6 What is the full name of the company known as 3M?

7 What product got its name from a slogan for Wrigley's saying 'Packed tight – Kept right'?

8 For what did Lewis Edson Waterman, a New York insurance broker, take out a patent in 1884?

9 For which product were people persuaded to 'Stop me and Buy one'?

10 To protect it from imitation, which Swiss chocolate bar was granted a patent in 1909?

11 What car manufacturer was founded in 1903?

12 Who patented the first revolver in 1836?

13 Which company began manufacturing their tennis rackets in 1881?

14 Who was Pretty Polly, from whom the stockings and tights manufacturer got its name?

15 Which drink product got its name from two of its ingredients, eggs and malt extract?

16 Who started a wholesale candy business in 1910 which has grown into a company that exports to 150 countries worldwide?

17 Which Polish-born immigrant started manufacturing and selling make-up in 1916?

18 Who invented the ball-point pen?

19 Which company came about from the merger between Lever Bros Ltd and the Dutch Margarine Union?

20 Which product was named by its founder, Ole Christiansen, after the Danish for 'play well'?

21 How did the name Kodak come about?

22 What everyday household item did Jacques Brandenberger invent in 1908?

23 Which headwear manufacturer took its name from the raw materials silk, angora and wool?

24 In 1925 Grace Scurr, a temporary secretary, named which product, now synonymous with the 1980s?

25 Which brothers made their first milk chocolate in 1897?

ANSWERS TO QUIZ 13

Teams
1 Anchorman
2 Harlem Globetrotters
3 Life-saving (he swims out with a line attached to his belt)
4 Driving a bullock team
5 The Dream Team
6 Crambo
7 Green Bay Packers
8 Ecurie or Equipe
9 'Mush'
10 The Brat Pack
11 Seahawks
12 New Zealand
13 Special teams
14 Robert Vaughn
15 A sled pulled by dogs
16 Seven
17 A passenger
18 Wild card (entry)
19 Uruguay
20 Chicago
21 Davis Cup
22 Seven
23 The Rat Pack
24 New York Mets
25 *Cool Runnings*

Alfred Hitchcock
1 He carries a double bass onto the train
2 *Rebecca*
3 *Marnie*
4 *Rear Window*
5 W Somerset Maugham
6 Gary Cooper
7 Salvador Dali
8 *Lifeboat*
9 Uranium ore
10 Joseph Cotten
11 *The Birds*
12 $40,000
13 James Stewart
14 *The Thirty-Nine Steps*
15 He adapted the story for the screen
16 *Saboteur*
17 Farley Granger
18 *Hamlet*
19 Honored 1967, received 1968
20 It was the first film completed by Hitchcock
21 *The Man who Knew Too Much*
22 Shirley MacLaine
23 *To Catch a Thief*
24 *Dial M for Murder*
25 Montgomery Clift

Africa
1 Sudan
2 Botswana
3 The Limpopo
4 Fifteen
5 The coral snake
6 Lake Victoria
7 Shoebill
8 Cairo
9 The springbok
10 The Sahara Desert
11 No, they inhabit the south and east
12 The Gulf of Aden
13 Tanzania
14 The Rift Valley
15 It is Africa's most northerly national park
16 Two (Mediterranean monk seal and Cape fur seal)
17 Greater and lesser flamingos
18 The Congo
19 Lion
20 The Nile crocodile
21 Gazelle
22 Six (Gabon, Congo, Democratic Republic of Congo, Uganda, Kenya and Somalia)
23 The Gambia
24 Tanzania
25 Elephant

Soul Music
1 'Save Your Sweet Love Just For Me'
2 Dusty Springfield
3 James Brown
4 Sam Cooke
5 The MGs (along with Booker T Jones)
6 James Brown (they are all mentioned in Arthur Conley's 'Sweet Soul Music')
7 Curtis Mayfield
8 Saxophone
9 Aaron Neville
10 Aretha Franklin
11 Green
12 Harlem ('The Harlem Shuffle')
13 Teddy Pendergrass
14 Isaac Hayes
15 Wilson Pickett
16 Earth Wind and Fire
17 Sam and Dave
18 '...I'm Black and I'm Proud'
19 The Staple Singers
20 *The Blues Brothers*
21 Gamble and Huff
22 Otis Redding
23 Isaac Hayes, 'Theme from *Shaft*'
24 Jackie Wilson
25 'Isn't She Lovely'

Politics
1 1920s (1928)
2 Nikita Krushchev
3 Warsaw Pact
4 Bobby Sands
5 The KGB
6 To save coal resources
7 Rhodesia
8 Northern Ireland
9 Margaret Thatcher
10 Democratic Party
11 The Cultural Revolution
12 1995
13 Paris
14 Mikhail Gorbachev
15 The 'Million Man March'
16 Robben Island
17 President Nasser of Egypt
18 Lord Beaverbrook
19 Fianna Fail
20 Zimbabwe African National Union
21 Michael Dukakis
22 Edward Heath
23 Nelson Mandela and F.W. de Klerk
24 Pol Pot
25 1957

Boxing
1 The 75th
2 James J Corbett
3 He became the first man to referee world title fights at every weight division
4 Gene Tunney, who went on to beat Jack Dempsey
5 Seventeen
6 The Marquess of Queensbury
7 Marvin Hagler
8 Jane Couch
9 Roberto Duran, 1980
10 Muhammad Ali (originally Cassius Clay)
11 Jersey Joe Walcott
12 Randolph Turpin
13 Ali v Foreman in Zaire, 1974
14 Jake LaMotta
15 It was the first world title fight to be filmed
16 Floyd Patterson, 1960
17 Chris Eubank
18 Julio Cesar Chavez
19 Thomas Hearns
20 Twenty-one
21 She was the first woman to judge a world title fight (Ali v Shavers, 1977)
22 Super heavyweight
23 Mike Tyson
24 Jim Watt
25 They both won three consecutive Olympic gold medals. Papp 1948, '52 and '56; Stevenson 1972, '76 and '80.

Animation
1 Scooby Doo
2 *King of the Hill*
3 Bam Bam
4 Bugs Bunny
5 *Family Guy*
6 *Wait 'til Your Father Gets Home*
7 Mel Blanc
8 Four
9 Schroeder
10 France/Gaul
11 Penelope Pitstop
12 Sylvester
13 Jellystone
14 Sgt Bilko
15 *Seinfeld*
16 Noo Noo
17 The name Michelangelo
18 Officer Dibble
19 Deputy Dawg
20 Bedrock
21 Mike Judge
22 The Archies
23 Mr Jinx
24 *South Park*
25 Fred Quimby

Brand Names
1 Ladies' underwear
2 Bovril
3 Clarence Birdseye
4 Coca-Cola
5 1960
6 The Minnesota Mining and Manufacturing Company
7 PK chewing gum
8 A fountain pen
9 Wall's ice cream
10 Toblerone
11 The Ford Motor Company
12 Samuel Colt
13 Slazenger
14 A successful racehorse
15 Ovaltine (Ovamaltine)
16 Franklin C Mars
17 Max Factor
18 Laszlo Biro
19 Unilever
20 Lego (leg godt)
21 Founder George Eastman wanted a name that started and ended with a 'k'
22 Cellophane
23 Kangol
24 Filofax
25 The Cadbury brothers

NOW THAT'S WHAT I CALL A TRIVIA BOOK

QUIZ 14

15

1 *The Heart of the Antarctic* (1909) and *South* (1919) were written by which leader of several Antarctic expeditions who died in 1922 at Grytviken, South Georgia?

2 What colour jersey is worn by the leader of the Tour de France?

3 Who is generally regarded as the leader of the Bolshevik Revolution?

4 Who led the expedition in 1953 which culminated with Hillary and Tenzing reaching the summit of Mount Everest?

5 Who preceded Neil Kinnock as leader of the British Labour Party?

6 Who, in 1866, became principal chief of the northern hunting Sioux, with Crazy Horse, leader of the Oglala Sioux, as his vice-chief?

7 Who was the leader of 'Operation Chastise' which in 1943 caused considerable damage to dams in Germany?

8 Shaka or Chaka was the leader of which people in the early 19th century?

9 What name is given to the British government minister whose responsibility is to manage its programme of business through the House?

10 Who led the Israelites to the Promised Land?

11 How is Karim Al-Hussain Shah, the leader of the Nizari Ismailite sect of Islam, better known?

12 Robert Leroy Parker was the leader of the 'Hole in the Wall Gang', also known as the 'Wild Bunch'. How is he better known?

13 Which instrument does the leader of an orchestra play?

14 Which 1965 single by the Shangri-Las featured Billy Joel on piano?

15 Which party in Northern Ireland is led by David Trimble?

16 Dante Gabriel Rossetti was one of the leaders of which art movement?

17 With the middle name Winston, who was the deputy leader of the British Labour Party from 1980 to 1983?

18 Which brothers were the leaders of the first Jutish settlers in Britain in the 5th century AD?

19 What name is given to a Hindu or Sikh religious teacher or leader giving personal spiritual guidance to his disciples?

20 What title was assumed by Mohammed Ahmed, Sudanese military leader, who led a revolt against Egypt and captured Khartoum in 1885?

21 Who was the leader of the Gunpowder Plot who was killed while resisting arrest?

22 What was the name of the English suffragette leader who founded the militant Women's Social and Political Union?

23 Who was the leader of Solidarity, later president of Poland, who won the Nobel Peace Prize in 1983?

24 Which English king led the Third Crusade in 1191?

25 What name is given to an article offered below cost in the hope that customers attracted by it will buy other goods?

1 Who won an Oscar for his performance in *High Noon*?

2 Who or what were Ethan (John Wayne) and Martin (Jeffrey Hunter) trying to find in John Ford's *The Searchers*?

3 Who played Billy the Kid in a) *Pat Garrett and Billy the Kid*, and b) *Young Guns*?

4 Who did Errol Flynn portray in *They Died with their Boots On*?

5 Which Bob Hope comedy western featured the Oscar-winning song 'Buttons and Bows'?

6 Who played Wyatt Earp in John Ford's *My Darling Clementine*?

7 Which director and leading actor are common to the following films: *Winchester '73*, *Bend in the River*, *The Naked Spur* and *The Man from Laramie*?

8 In the 1939 movie *Jesse James*, who played the roles of Jesse and his brother, Frank, respectively?

9 In which of Clint Eastwood's films does Chief Dan George tell him that white men have been 'sneaking up on us for years'?

10 On which film was the TV series *Alias Smith and Jones* based?

11 Which film did Orson Welles credit above all others with showing him how to direct a movie?

12 Which film was a remake of Akira Kurosawa's *Shichinin no Samurai*?

13 Who directed *The Unforgiven*?

14 Who won an Oscar for his twin roles in the 1965 film *Cat Ballou*?

15 Which famous dancer and choreographer directed *The Cheyenne Social Club* in 1970?

16 Who sang 'See What the Boys in the Back Room Will Have' in *Destry Rides Again*?

17 What was the name of the one-eyed character played by John Wayne in *True Grit*?

18 Which comedy duo went *Way Out West* in 1930?

19 Who was the star of the 1953 movie *Shane*?

20 Who played opposite Clint Eastwood in *Two Mules for Sister Sara* in 1969?

21 Who became a star in Howard Hughes's *The Outlaw*?

22 Which actor 'aged' to 121 years old in *Little Big Man*?

23 What was John Wayne's final film?

24 Which Apache Indian chief was played by Chuck Connors in 1962?

25 What was Dodge City renamed in *Carry On Cowboy*?

1 Palaeontologist Sir Richard Owen is credited with coining the name 'dinosaur' in 1841. From Greek origin, what is the rough translation of the term?

2 What were pterosaurs?

3 Which creature had two rows of plates running down its neck, back and tail, culminating in large spikes at the tail end?

4 Why was the Seismosaurus so named?

5 As stipulated by the International Code of Zoological Nomenclature, dinosaur names are in two parts, the first part being the genus. What is denoted by the second part?

6 Which creature had a short nose horn and two larger horns on its brow?

7 Which creature's name has passed out of usage after it was discovered that its fossils proved to be identical to the previously named Apatosaurus?

8 Why was the Edmontosaurus so named?

9 What is the significance of the Megalosaurus?

10 What was the largest of all the carnivorous dinosaurs?

11 Dinosaurs lived in the Mesozoic Era, between 65 and 290 million years ago. Split into three periods, which came between the Triassic and Cretaceous periods?

12 Which British pop group had a hit with 'Brontosaurus'?

13 As their names would suggest, where were the Mamenchisaurus and the Tuojiangosaurus found?

14 Archaeopteryx differed from its modern counterparts in that it had teeth, clawed fingers and a bony tail core. Otherwise it bore the characteristics of which group of creatures?

15 Which creature got its name because scientists felt that it fed on eggs?

16 Why do fossils of long-necked dinosaurs appear to show the head pulled back over the body?

17 Which is the smallest living dinosaur?

18 Which came off better in a fight, Tyrannosaurus rex or Iguanadon?

19 On which modern continent did Tyrannosaurus live?

20 In which period did the Diplodocus live?

21 In which American state is the Dinosaur Valley Museum?

22 In what environment did ichthyosaurs live?

23 Which cartoon family have a pet dinosaur called Dino?

24 Why was the Psittacosaurus so called?

25 Featured in the film *Jurassic Park*, which creature's name means 'quick plunderer'?

1 Which lyricist worked with Richard Rodgers on such songs as 'Blue Moon', 'Where or When' and 'My Funny Valentine'?

2 Which of Carole King's songs gave James Taylor a big hit in 1971?

3 Writer for Michael Jackson, George Benson and Michael McDonald among others, with which band did Rod Temperton first find success?

4 A hit for Elvis Costello in 1999, who wrote and had a UK number one with 'She' in 1974?

5 Who had a hit with Costello's 'Girls Talk'?

6 Whose songs have been successful for Guns N' Roses, Manfred Mann and Jimi Hendrix?

7 Which Motown artist wrote the songs 'My Guy' by Mary Wells and 'My Girl' by The Temptations?

8 Who was the first person to cover a Lennon/McCartney song?

9 Which American songwriter co-wrote Abba's 'Ring Ring'?

10 Who has written songs with Mike Love, Tony Asher and Van Dyke Parks?

11 Which songwriters and musicians are the core of Steely Dan?

12 Which songwriting duo wrote a string of rock and roll classics, including 'Hound Dog', 'Stand By Me', 'Up on the Roof' and 'Broadway'?

8

13 Which UK number one by Marvin Gaye was written by Norman Whitfield and Barrett Strong?

14 The song 'Evergreen' was a big hit for Barbra Streisand. Did she write the words or the music?

15 What is the surname of the brothers who wrote, among others, 'Chim Chim Cheree', 'Chitty Chitty Bang Bang' and 'The Bare Necessities'?

16 With which renowned American composer did Elvis Costello collaborate on the 1998 album *Painted from Memory*?

17 Which songwriters connect David Bowie, Chris Farlowe, Melanie, and Marianne Faithfull?

18 Who co-wrote the Band Aid single 'Do They Know It's Christmas'?

19 Who wrote the American counterpart 'We Are the World'?

20 Who immortalised the 1969 Woodstock festival in song?

21 Which Henry Mancini/Johnny Mercer song was 'sung' by Audrey Hepburn in *Breakfast at Tiffany's*?

22 A huge hit for Whitney Houston, who wrote 'I Will Always Love You'?

23 Which team, later married, wrote 'Ain't No Mountain High Enough', 'Reach Out and Touch' and 'You're All I Need to Get By'?

24 Which song was George Harrison accused of plagiarising for his hit 'My Sweet Lord'?

25 Whose songs were recorded by a variety of artists on the album *Red Hot and Blue*?

1 Imprisoned since 1962, who walked free from captivity in February 1990?

2 Which pop star died from an AIDS-related illness in November 1991?

3 Who opened the Channel Tunnel in 1994?

4 In which year did Germany celebrate reunification?

5 In which year was John McCarthy released by his Lebanese captors?

6 Which world-famous musician died on 1 December 1997?

7 Who became Russia's first democratically elected president in 1991?

8 In which city was George Michael arrested for lewd behaviour in a public toilet?

9 Whom did Elvis Presley's daughter Lisa Marie marry in 1994?

10 In 1997, Zaire was renamed by its president, Laurent Kabila. What is its current full title?

11 When she died on 4 August 1997, Jeanne Caldwell was the world's oldest person. How old was she?

12 Which former Mrs Phillips became a Mrs Laurence in 1992?

13 To what name did the city of Leningrad revert in 1991?

14 Of which organisation did Boutros Boutros-Ghali become secretary-general in 1992?

15 Who was at the centre of a televised trial lasting 266 days in 1995?

16 In which year was the Warsaw Pact dissolved?

17 Released in 1995, what was the first entirely computer-generated feature film?

18 In which year did the siege of Waco take place?

19 What sparked the 1992 riots in Los Angeles?

20 In which year did the Spice Girls first enter the UK charts?

21 What significant action was taken in the Middle East on 2 August 1990?

22 In which year was Nelson Mandela elected president of South Africa?

23 What was opened on 6 May 1994?

24 Who recorded the biggest-selling single of all time in 1997?

25 Which Israeli leader was assassinated by a Jewish extremist in 1995?

8

1 Which team didn't collect the trophy in the first FA Cup final in 1872?

2 In the final of which indoor sport's world championship was Ronnie Baxter well and truly beaten in January 2000?

3 Who were the beaten finalists in the 1991 Rugby Union World Cup, held in England?

4 Who was beaten in consecutive Wimbledon singles finals in the 1980s by Boris Becker and Pat Cash?

5 Although arguably the greatest 800 metres runner of all time, who managed only silver medals in the event at the Moscow and Los Angeles Olympics?

6 Which country contested three of the first four European Football Championship finals, losing them all?

7 Who has lost in all six of his World Professional Snooker Championship finals?

8 Which team lost two consecutive Worthington Cup finals in the 1990s?

9 What connects Garrison Savannah in 1991, Party Politics in 1995 and Blue Charm in 1999?

10 Who came second in an athletics race at the Seoul Olympics and took home the gold medal?

11 Who were beaten by Australia in the final of the 1999 Cricket World Cup?

12 Which footballing nation has been beaten in three World Cup finals?

13 Who were runners-up in the FA Carling Premiership in 1994/95 and 1997/98?

14 Who lost to John Daly in the play-off for the 1995 Open Golf Championship, after sinking an incredible putt on the 72nd hole to tie the scores?

15 Who reached three Wimbledon finals in the 1990s and was thwarted first by Andre Agassi and then twice by Pete Sampras?

16 Who were the first runners-up in the Football League Cup in 1961, in the days before many top teams were involved?

17 Despite winning more races than champion Mike Hawthorn, who was runner-up in the 1958 Formula One season?

18 A Wimbledon champion three times, in how many other finals was Boris Becker on the receiving end?

19 Which rugby union side was beaten by Toulouse in the first Heineken European Cup final in 1996?

20 Which American football team were beaten finalists in four consecutive Superbowls in the 1990s?

21 What do Ilie Nastase, Jimmy Connors, Roscoe Tanner and John McEnroe have in common?

22 Who were runners-up in the University Boat Race in 2000?

23 The United States topped the medal table at the first modern Olympics at Athens in 1896. Which nation came second?

24 In *Wisden*, the bible of cricket, a panel of 100 experts voted Sir Donald Bradman player of the century. Who came second in the poll?

25 Old Etonians were first in 1875 and Sheffield Wednesday the most recent in 1993 – to do what?

4

1 Which legendary frontiersman did Fess Parker play on TV in the late 1950s?

2 In which 1980s soap opera did a woman once married to Ronald Reagan play Angela Channing?

3 Billy Crystal played a transvestite in which US sitcom first transmitted in the late 1970s?

4 Who played Zorro in the 1958–60 TV series?

5 James Drury, Lee J. Cobb and Doug McClure starred in the first TV western to run for 90 minutes per episode. What was it called?

6 Ted Cassidy played which family's butler?

7 Before *The X-Files*, David Duchovny had appeared in another cult TV series that dealt with the paranormal. What was it called?

8 Only one cast member of the movie *M*A*S*H* reprised his role in the TV series. Who?

9 Tom Selleck played Lance White, a rival of which US private eye?

10 After restoring his ears to normal, Leonard Nimoy played a character with the name of a capital city in which adventure series?

11 Actress Rhea Perlman married her husband Danny DeVito during a lunchbreak on which TV series?

12 Ralph James provided the voice of Orson in which 70s/80s sitcom?

13 Edward Asner first played Lou Grant in which 1970s show?

14 Ron Ely starred as Tarzan on TV between 1967–69, but who provided the Lord of the Jungle's famous jungle yell for the series?

15 Which husband-and-wife team appeared in Space 1999?

16 The narrator of 1980s sci-fi TV series *Buck Rogers in the 25th Century* played a top TV detective in the previous decade. Who was he?

17 Burgess Meredith occasionally appeared as a 'pompous, waddling perpetrator of foul play' in which classic TV series?

18 Honor Blackman and Diana Rigg played two of Patrick Macnee's sidekicks in the 1960s TV series *The Avengers*. Who played the third?

19 Raymond Francis played Tom Lockhart in *Murder Bag*, *Crime Sheet* and which other series?

20 Veteran British actor Wilfrid Hyde-White played scientist Dr Goodfellow in which 1980s space opera?

21 One actor appeared in both the *A-Team* and *Battlestar Galactica*. Who was he?

22 Sharon Gless, later to find fame in *Cagney & Lacey*, played nurse Kathleen Feverty in which 60s/70s medical series?

23 Before he became known for providing the voices on Hanna-Barbera cartoons, Mel Blanc regularly appeared on a famous 1950s comedy show. What was it?

24 In which 50s/60s classic comedy series did Paul Ford play Colonel John Hall?

25 The novelist Colin Dexter appeared as an extra in every episode of which TV series?

1 In which decade of the 19th century did Conservative Judaism separate from Reform in the United States?

2 Who in 1534 proclaimed himself head of the Church of England?

3 What does the Arabic word 'Islam' mean?

4 Which religion developed in ancient Persia more than a thousand years before Islam?

5 Which branch of Christianity was pioneered by the brothers John and Charles Wesley and George Whitefield in the late 1720s?

6 Which tradition originated at the end of the 15th century in northern India?

7 A Bar Mitzvah ceremony celebrates a boy's coming of age at thirteen. What is the ceremony called when a girl reaches that age?

8 By what nickname are followers of the Holy Spirit Association for the Unification of World Christianity better known?

9 What do Buddhists call the state of final and definitive enlightenment?

10 The swastika symbol is sacred to the Jain tradition. What is meant by the Sanskrit word 'svastika'?

11 In which year was Pakistan formed as an Islamic state?

12 Which branch of Christianity holds meetings in Kingdom Halls?

13 Which order was founded in Boston, Massachusetts in 1879 by Mary Baker Eddy after receiving help from a healer for her spinal condition?

14 'Kippah' is the Hebrew word for the skullcap worn by Jews. What is the equivalent Yiddish word?

15 In which country do people worship nature deities and spirits in a tradition called Shrine Shinto?

16 In which century did the Dalai Lamas become rulers of Tibet?

17 The *Bhagavad-Gita* is a holy book of which religion?

18 What is meant by Rosh Hashanah?

19 Of which religion is Sufism a branch?

20 Which order is referred to as 'fire worshippers' by its detractors?

21 What occasion in the Christian calendar is the first Sunday after the first full moon after the spring equinox?

22 In which Asian capital city is the Temple of Heaven?

23 What is the meaning of the word 'Shinto'?

24 Which religion has a doctrine of the 'three bodies', consisting of the Appearance or Transformation Body, the Body of Bliss and the Dharma Body?

25 What name is given to the Islamic period of fasting?

22

ANSWERS TO QUIZ 14

Leaders

1 Sir Ernest Shackleton
2 Yellow
3 Vladimir Ilyich Lenin
4 Sir John Hunt
5 Michael Foot
6 Sitting Bull
7 Guy Gibson
8 Zulu
9 Leader of the House
10 Moses
11 Aga Khan
12 Butch Cassidy
13 Violin
14 'Leader of the Pack'
15 Ulster Unionists
16 Pre-Raphaelite Brotherhood
17 Dennis Healey
18 Hengist and Horsa
19 Guru
20 The Mahdi
21 Robert Catesby
22 Emmeline Pankhurst
23 Lech Walesa
24 Richard I (Coeur de Lion)
25 Loss leader

Westerns

1 Gary Cooper
2 Ethan's niece, Debbie (Natalie Wood)
3 a) Kris Kristofferson, b) Emilio Estevez
4 General George Armstrong Custer
5 *The Paleface*
6 Henry Fonda
7 Anthony Mann and James Stewart
8 Tyrone Power and Henry Fonda
9 *The Outlaw Josey Wales*
10 *Butch Cassidy and the Sundance Kid*
11 John Ford's *Stagecoach*
12 *The Magnificent Seven*
13 John Huston, 1960 (Clint Eastwood's film is called *Unforgiven*)
14 Lee Marvin
15 Gene Kelly
16 Marlene Dietrich
17 Rooster Cogburn
18 Laurel and Hardy
19 Alan Ladd
20 Shirley MacLaine
21 Jane Russell
22 Dustin Hoffman
23 *The Shootist*
24 Geronimo
25 Stodge City

Dinosaurs

1 Terrible lizard (*deinos sauros*)
2 Warm-blooded flying reptiles related to dinosaurs
3 Stegosaurus
4 Because of its size, hence 'earth-shaking lizard'
5 Species
6 Triceratops
7 Brontosaurus
8 Its remains were first discovered in Edmonton, Canada
9 It was the first formally recognised dinosaur to be given a name
10 Tyrannosaurus rex
11 The Jurassic period
12 The Move
13 China
14 Birds
15 Oviraptor
16 Shrinkage of neck muscles after death
17 The bee hummingbird
18 Neither; they missed each other by about 42 million years
19 North America
20 Jurassic
21 Colorado
22 Water
23 The Flintstones
24 It had a short head with a parrot-like beak
25 Velociraptor

Songwriters

1 Lorenz Hart
2 'You've Got a Friend'
3 Heatwave
4 Charles Aznavour
5 Dave Edmunds
6 Bob Dylan
7 Smokey Robinson
8 Kenny Lynch with 'Misery'
9 Neil Sedaka
10 Brian Wilson
11 Walter Becker and Donald Fagen
12 Jerry Leiber and Mike Stoller
13 'I Heard It Through the Grapevine'
14 Music
15 Sherman (Richard M and Robert R)
16 Burt Bacharach
17 Mick Jagger and Keith Richards
18 Bob Geldof and Midge Ure
19 Michael Jackson and Lionel Richie
20 Joni Mitchell
21 'Moon River'
22 Dolly Parton
23 Nickolas Ashford and Valerie Simpson
24 'He's So Fine'
25 Cole Porter

The 1990s

1 Nelson Mandela
2 Freddie Mercury
3 The Queen and François Mitterrand
4 1990
5 1991
6 Stéphane Grappelli
7 Boris Yeltsin
8 Los Angeles
9 Michael Jackson
10 The Democratic Republic of Congo
11 *Reservoir Dogs*
12 Princess Anne
13 St Petersburg
14 The United Nations
15 O J Simpson
16 1991
17 *Toy Story*
18 Clockwork radio
19 The acquittal of Rodney King's police attackers
20 1996
21 Iraq invaded Kuwait
22 1994
23 The Channel Tunnel
24 Elton John
25 Yitzhak Rabin

Runners-Up

1 Royal Engineers (they lost the next two as well)
2 Darts (he lost to Ted Hankey)
3 England
4 Ivan Lendl
5 Sebastian Coe
6 Yugoslavia
7 Jimmy White
8 Middlesbrough
9 They all came second in the Grand National
10 Carl Lewis (after Ben Johnson's disqualification)
11 122
12 West Germany (1966, 1982 and 1986)
13 Man Utd
14 Costantino Rocca
15 Goran Ivanisevic
16 Rotherham United (lost 3-2 to Aston Villa)
17 Stirling Moss
Four (1988, 1989, 1991 and 1994)
18 1993
19 Cardiff
20 Buffalo Bills
21 They were all beaten in Wimbledon finals by Borg
22 Cambridge
23 Greece
24 Sir Garfield Sobers
25 They lost the FA Cup final after a replay

Cast List

1 Davy Crockett
2 *Falcon Crest* (Jane Wyman)
3 *Soap*
4 Guy Williams
5 *The Virginian*
6 The Addams family
7 *Twin Peaks*
8 Gary Burghoff as Radar
9 Jim Rockford
10 *Mission: Impossible* (playing Paris)
11 *Taxi*
12 *Mork & Mindy*
13 *The Mary Tyler Moore Show*
14 Johnny Weismuller
15 Martin Landau and Barbara Bain
16 *William Conrad, alias Frank Cannon*
17 *Batman*
18 Linda Thorson
19 *No Hiding Place*
20 *Buck Rogers in the 25th Century*
21 Dirk Benedict
22 *Marcus Welby MD*
23 *The Jack Benny Show*
24 *The Phil Silvers Show*
25 *Inspector Morse*

Religion

1 The 1880s (1889)
2 Henry VIII
3 Submission or surrender
4 Zoroastrianism
5 Methodism
6 The Sikh tradition
7 Bat Mitzvah
8 Moonies
9 Nirvana
10 Well-being
11 1947
12 Jehovah's Witnesses
13 The Church of Christ, Scientist
14 Yarmulke
15 Japan
16 Seventeenth
17 Hinduism
18 Jewish New Year
19 Islam
20 Zoroastrians
21 Easter
22 Beijing
23 The way of the gods
24 Mahayana Buddhism
25 Ramadan